Government–Industry Partnerships for the Development of New Technologies

Charles W. Wessner, Editor

Board on Science, Technology, and Economic Policy

Policy and Global Affairs

NATIONAL RESEARCH COUNCIL
OF THE NATIONAL ACADEMIES

THE NATIONAL ACADEMIES PRESS
Washington, D.C.
www.nap.edu

THE NATIONAL ACADEMIES PRESS 500 Fifth Street, NW Washington, D.C. 20001

NOTICE: The project that is the subject of this report was approved by the Governing Board of the National Research Council, whose members are drawn from the councils of the National Academy of Sciences, the National Academy of Engineering, and the Institute of Medicine. The members of the committee responsible for the report were chosen for their special competences and with regard for appropriate balance.

Any opinions, findings, conclusions, or recommendations expressed in this publication are those of the author(s) and do not necessarily reflect the views of the organizations or agencies that provided support for the project.

International Standard Book Number 0-309-08502-0

Additional copies of this report are available from National Academies Press, 500 Fifth Street, N.W., Lockbox 285, Washington, D.C. 20055; (800) 624-6242 or (202) 334-3313 (in the Washington metropolitan area); Internet, http://www.nap.edu

Printed in the United States of America

THE NATIONAL ACADEMIES

Advisers to the Nation on Science, Engineering, and Medicine

The **National Academy of Sciences** is a private, nonprofit, self-perpetuating society of distinguished scholars engaged in scientific and engineering research, dedicated to the furtherance of science and technology and to their use for the general welfare. Upon the authority of the charter granted to it by the Congress in 1863, the Academy has a mandate that requires it to advise the federal government on scientific and technical matters. Dr. Bruce M. Alberts is president of the National Academy of Sciences.

The **National Academy of Engineering** was established in 1964, under the charter of the National Academy of Sciences, as a parallel organization of outstanding engineers. It is autonomous in its administration and in the selection of its members, sharing with the National Academy of Sciences the responsibility for advising the federal government. The National Academy of Engineering also sponsors engineering programs aimed at meeting national needs, encourages education and research, and recognizes the superior achievements of engineers. Dr. Wm. A. Wulf is president of the National Academy of Engineering.

The **Institute of Medicine** was established in 1970 by the National Academy of Sciences to secure the services of eminent members of appropriate professions in the examination of policy matters pertaining to the health of the public. The Institute acts under the responsibility given to the National Academy of Sciences by its congressional charter to be an adviser to the federal government and, upon its own initiative, to identify issues of medical care, research, and education. Dr. Harvey V. Fineberg is president of the Institute of Medicine.

The **National Research Council** was organized by the National Academy of Sciences in 1916 to associate the broad community of science and technology with the Academy's purposes of furthering knowledge and advising the federal government. Functioning in accordance with general policies determined by the Academy, the Council has become the principal operating agency of both the National Academy of Sciences and the National Academy of Engineering in providing services to the government, the public, and the scientific and engineering communities. The Council is administered jointly by both Academies and the Institute of Medicine. Dr. Bruce M. Alberts and Dr. Wm. A. Wulf are chair and vice chair, respectively, of the National Research Council.

www.national-academies.org

Steering Committee for Government-Industry Partnerships for the Development of New Technologies*

Gordon Moore, *Chair*
Chairman Emeritus, *retired*
Intel Corporation

M. Kathy Behrens
Managing Director of Medical Technology
Robertson Stephens Investment Management and STEP Board

Michael Borrus
Managing Director
The Petkevich Group, LLC

Iain M. Cockburn
Professor of Finance and Economics
Boston University

Kenneth Flamm
Dean Rusk Chair in International Affairs
LBJ School of Public Affairs
University of Texas at Austin

James F. Gibbons
Professor of Engineering
Stanford University

W. Clark McFadden
Partner
Dewey Ballantine

Burton J. McMurtry
General Partner, *retired*
Technology Venture Investors

William J. Spencer, *Vice-Chair*
Chairman Emeritus
International SEMATECH and STEP Board

Mark B. Myers
Senior Vice-President, *retired*
Xerox Corporation and STEP Board

Richard Nelson
George Blumenthal Professor of International and Public Affairs
Columbia University

Edward E. Penhoet
Chief Program Officer, Science and Higher Education
Gordon and Betty Moore Foundation and STEP Board

Charles Trimble
Chairman
U.S. GPS Industry Council

John P. Walker
Chairman and Chief Executive Officer
Axys Pharmaceuticals, Inc.

Patrick Windham
President, Windham Consulting and Lecturer, Stanford University

---

*As of March 2002.

Project Staff*

Charles W. Wessner
Study Director

Sujai J. Shivakumar
Program Officer

Adam Korobow
Program Officer

Alan Anderson
Consultant

David E. Dierksheide
Program Associate

Christopher S. Hayter
Program Associate

Tabitha M. Benney
Program Associate

McAlister T. Clabaugh
Program Associate

---

*As of March 2002. In the course of this extensive review of Government-Industry Partnerships, several other staff contributed to our work. These include John B. Horrigan, John Oldfield, Ryan Catteau, and Laura Holiday.

For the National Research Council (NRC), this project was overseen by the Board on Science, Technology, and Economic Policy (STEP), a standing board of the NRC established by the National Academies of Sciences and Engineering and the Institute of Medicine in 1991. The mandate of the STEP Board is to integrate understanding of scientific, technological, and economic elements in the formulation of national policies to promote the economic well-being of the United States. A distinctive characteristic of STEP's approach is its frequent interactions with public and private-sector decision makers. STEP bridges the disciplines of business management, engineering, economics, and the social sciences to bring diverse expertise to bear on pressing public policy questions. The members of the STEP Board* and the NRC staff are listed below.

Dale Jorgenson, *Chair*
Frederic Eaton Abbe Professor
of Economics
Harvard University

William J. Spencer, *Vice-Chair*
Chairman Emeritus
International SEMATECH

M. Kathy Behrens
Managing Director of Medical Technology
Robertson Stephens Investment
Management

Bronwyn Hall
Professor of Economics
University of California at Berkeley

James Heckman
Henry Schultz Distinguished Service
Professor of Economics
University of Chicago

Ralph Landau
Consulting Professor of Economics
Stanford University

Richard Levin
President
Yale University

David T. Morgenthaler
Founding Partner
Morgenthaler

Mark B. Myers
Senior Vice-President, *retired*
Xerox Corporation

Roger Noll
Morris M. Doyle Centennial
Professor of Economics
Stanford University

Edward E. Penhoet
Chief Program Officer, Science and Higher Education
Gordon and Betty Moore Foundation

William Raduchel
Chief Technology Officer
AOL Time Warner

Alan Wm. Wolff
Managing Partner
Dewey Ballantine

*As of March 2002.

STEP Staff*

Stephen A. Merrill
Executive Director

Charles W. Wessner
Program Director

Sujai J. Shivakumar
Program Officer

Adam K. Korobow
Program Officer

Craig M. Schultz
Research Associate

Tabitha Benney
Program Associate

Camille M. Collett
Program Associate

Christopher S. Hayter
Program Associate

David Dierksheide
Program Associate

McAlister Clabaugh
Program Associate

*As of March 2002.

National Research Council
Board on Science, Technology, and Economic Policy

Sponsors

The National Research Council gratefully acknowledges the support of the following sponsors:

National Aeronautics and Space Administration

Office of the Director, Defense Research & Engineering

National Science Foundation

U.S. Department of Energy

Office of Naval Research

National Institutes of Health

National Institute of Standards and Technology

Sandia National Laboratories

Electric Power Research Institute

International Business Machines

Kulicke and Soffa Industries

Merck and Company

Milliken Industries

Motorola

Nortel

Procter and Gamble

Silicon Valley Group, Incorporated

Advanced Micro Devices

Reports in the Series

Government-Industry Partnerships for the Development of New Technologies

New Vistas in Transatlantic Science and Technology Cooperation
Washington, D.C.: National Academy Press, 1999.

Industry-Laboratory Partnerships: A Review of the Sandia Science and Technology Park Initiative
Washington, D.C.: National Academy Press, 1999.

The Advanced Technology Program: Challenges and Opportunities
Washington, D.C.: National Academy Press, 1999.

The Small Business Innovation Research Program: Challenges and Opportunities
Washington, D.C.: National Academy Press, 1999.

The Small Business Innovation Research Program: An Assessment of the Department of Defense Fast Track Initiative
Washington, D.C.: National Academy Press, 2000.

A Review of the New Initiatives at the NASA Ames Research Center
Washington, D.C.: National Academy Press, 2001.

The Advanced Technology Program: Assessing Outcomes
Washington, D.C.: National Academy Press, 2001.

Capitalizing on New Needs and New Opportunities: Government-Industry Partnerships in Biotechnology and Information Technology
Washington, D.C.: National Academy Press, 2002.

Partnerships for Solid-State Lighting
Washington, D.C.: National Academy Press, 2002.

Securing the Future: Regional and National Programs to Support the Semiconductor Industry
Washington, D.C.: National Academy Press, (forthcoming).

Contents

BOXES

FIGURES

Preface

The mission of the National Research Council's Board on Science, Technology, and Economic Policy (STEP) is to improve policy makers' understanding of the interconnections between science, technology, and economic policy, and their importance to the American economy. The STEP Board's activities reflect the increased recognition of the importance of technology to economic growth. In recent years public-private partnerships to develop new technologies have played an increased role both in the United States and abroad. In the United States, partnerships are sometimes controversial. The premise of this study is that an objective analysis could lead to a better understanding of the contributions and limitations of partnerships.

To further our understanding of the motivations, operations, and policy challenges associated with public-private partnerships, the STEP Board launched a major review of U.S. and foreign programs. This program-based analysis is led by Gordon Moore, Chairman Emeritus of Intel, and Bill Spencer, Chairman Emeritus of International SEMATECH, and carried out by a distinguished multidisciplinary Steering Committee that includes members from academia, high-technology industries, venture capital firms, and the realm of public policy.[1] Topics taken up by the Committee on Government-Industry Partnerships for the Development of New Technologies include the drivers of cooperation among industry, government, and universities; operational assessments of current programs; emerging needs at the intersection of biotechnology and information technology; the current experience of foreign government partnerships and opportu-

[1]The members of the Steering Committee are listed in the front matter of this volume.

nities for international cooperation; and the changing roles of government laboratories, universities, and other research organizations.

PROJECT PARAMETERS

The Committee's analysis has included a significant but necessarily limited portion of the variety of cooperative activity that takes place between the government and the private sector.[2] The Committee's desire to carry out an analysis of current partnerships that is directly relevant to contemporary policy making has conditioned the selection of the specific programs reviewed. The study, in addition, has focused on "best practices" as a way of drawing out positive guidance for future public policy. Reports in the series, as well as this Summary Report, have therefore focused attention on conditions for success rather than on analyzing failures.

The Committee also recognizes the importance of placing each of the studies in the broader context of U.S. technology policy, which continues to employ a wide variety of *ad hoc* mechanisms that have evolved through the government's decentralized decision-making and management process. To meet its objective of policy-relevant analysis, the Committee has focused on the assessment of current and proposed programs, drawing on the experience of previous U.S. initiatives, foreign practices, and emerging areas resulting from federal investments in advanced technologies.[3]

Finally, the Committee has chosen to make policy recommendations and not operational prescriptions regarding specific public-private partnerships. Given the enormous variety in the size and scope of partnerships found in the United States, a detailed list of recommendations is simply not feasible or appropriate. The specific standards of operational success vary with the technologies, goals, and participants. Recognizing the limits imposed by this diversity, the Committee has chosen to highlight general positive recommendations rather than to attempt to develop specific blueprints; there is no "one size fits all" approach.

---

[2]For example, aside from SEMATECH (where DARPA served as the government partner) and broader references to DARPA's role in the development of the Internet, DARPA's programs and contributions have not been specifically reviewed. For an overview of the scope of cooperative activity at the federal and state levels, see C. Coburn and D. Berglund, *Partnerships: A Compendium of State and Federal Cooperative Technology Programs,* Columbus, OH: Battelle Press, 1995; and the RaDiUS database. See <http://www.rand.org/services/radius/>.

[3]The Committee has focused its attention on "best practices" rather than the practices of less successful partnerships, although it is certainly true that much can be learned from failures as well as successes. For an analysis of lessons that might be learned from comparing the experience of a less successful and a successful partnership, see John B. Horrigan, "Cooperating Competitors: A Comparison of MCC and SEMATECH." Monograph, Washington, D.C.: National Research Council, 1999.

The Committee's analysis divides among four primary areas. These are current U.S. partnership programs, potential U.S. partnership programs, industry-national laboratory partnerships, and international collaboration and benchmarking. The analysis of current U.S. partnerships has focused on two innovation and award programs, the Small Business Innovation Research program and the Advanced Technology Program. The review of potential partnerships for specific technologies, based on the project's extensive generic partnership analysis, has focused on needs in biotechnology, computing, and solid-state lighting. The industry-laboratory analysis has reviewed the potential and assessed policy challenges of science and technology parks at Sandia National Laboratories and the NASA Ames Research Center. The Committee's focus on international collaboration and benchmarking has included a wide review of new opportunities resulting from the U.S.-E.U. Science and Technology Agreement. In addition, the Committee documented and collaboratively reviewed programs at the regional and national level that had been designed to support the semiconductor industry, with a focus on Japan, Europe, Taiwan, and the United States. The need to work together in addressing common challenges, even as national technology programs support competing firms, is an overarching theme of the Committee's analysis.

Although interrelated, these analyses were self-contained and did not address the question of optimal allocation of funding among programs.[4] Practical policy relevance has been a guiding principle. A series of 10 intermediate reports on these programs and topics has already been published by the National Academies.[5] In general, the Committee's analysis of partnerships has focused attention on the operation of partnerships—the lessons they offer and how to apply those lessons, both positive and negative—to make partnerships more effective. Given this pragmatic orientation, the study did not (and was not intended to) take up the issue of whether partnerships should exist (they do), and the study was not designed to make comparisons between different partnership programs. Instead, the Committee's charge has been to take a pragmatic approach to address such issues as the rationale and organizing principles of public-private partnerships, current practices, sectoral differences, means of evaluation, the experience of foreign-based partnerships, and the roles of government laboratories, universities, and other non-profit organizations.

Given the depth, breadth, and complexity of this subject, and the number of intermediate reports already published as part of the STEP Board's larger project,

[4]Political realities of Congressional oversight, departmental authority and responsibilities, and existing constituencies often make recommendations for the reallocation of funds problematic. Moreover, the diversity of U.S. programs is one of the U.S. innovation system's strengths. Different programs often address different points in the innovation system.

[5]The 10 publications in this series are listed in the front matter.

an important purpose of this summary report is to explain, organize, and emphasize the key findings and recommendations of the earlier reports, and the Committee views on the project as a whole, for the benefit of policymakers. Most important to emphasize are the common threads that appear within the analysis of different partnerships.

The Committee's desire to ensure that its deliberations and analysis are directly relevant to current policy making has allowed it to be responsive to requests from the Executive Branch and the U.S. Congress to examine various policies and programs of current policy relevance. Policy-relevant analyses include a response to the White House and State Department request for an evaluation of opportunities for greater transatlantic cooperation—in order to better capitalize on the U.S.-E.U. Agreement on Science and Technology Cooperation. It includes as well a response to a request by the Defense Department's Under Secretary for Technology and Acquisitions to review the Small Business Innovation Research program's Fast Track initiative at the Department of Defense. Also included in the Committee portfolio of activities is the assessment of the Advanced Technology Program (ATP), requested by the National Institute of Standards and Technology (NIST) in compliance with Senate Report 105-235. The ATP program was the subject of two Committee reports: The first describes the program's goals, operations, and challenges. The second report assessed the operations and achievements of the program, and made suggestions on how to improve what was found to be an effective partnership program.[6]

There is broad support for this type of objective analysis among federal agencies and the private sector. Federal agencies that provided support for this analysis include the National Aeronautics and Space Administration, the U.S. Department of Defense, the U.S. Department of Energy, the National Science Foundation, the National Institutes of Health (especially the National Cancer Institute and the National Institute of General Medical Sciences), the Office of Naval Research, and the National Institute of Standards and Technology. Sandia National Laboratories and the Electric Power Research Institute (EPRI) have also provided important contributions. Support has also come from a diverse group of 10 private corporations.[7]

The conclusion of this intensive program-based study enables us to look at the multiple examples of public-private partnerships in the United States and elsewhere with informed perspective. The purpose of this final report is to highlight the larger issues and to summarize the insights gained through this analysis of partnerships, with the goal of generating a fuller, more informed appreciation

[6]See Senate Report 105-235, Departments of Commerce, Justice, and State, the Judiciary, and Related Agencies Appropriation Bill, 1999, and the Report from the Committee on Appropriations to accompany Bill S. 2260, which included the Commerce Department FY1999 Appropriations Bill.

[7]The complete list of sponsors is listed in the front matter of this report.

of past, current, and potential contributions of partnerships to the welfare, competitiveness, and security of the United States.

ACKNOWLEDGEMENTS

On behalf of the National Academies, we express our appreciation and recognition for the insights, experiences, and perspectives made available by the participants of various conferences.

A number of individuals deserve recognition for their contributions to the preparation of this summary report, the eleventh produced by the project. Among the STEP staff, Dr. Sujai Shivakumar played a major role in the preparation of this report, showing great skill in drawing together the disparate elements of this multifaceted assessment of public-private partnerships. He also frequently contributed original research and his own valuable insights. His colleague, Christopher Hayter, brought his enthusiasm, commitment, and considerable skill to the project to ensure the accuracy and quality of the report as well as its timely production. The study as a whole owes a great debt to McAlister Clabaugh and David Dierksheide, both of whom worked long, hard, and well over several years to hold the meetings and produce the reports required by this broad-based review. Their ability to master multiple priorities and provide uncompromising quality made the project possible. Without their collective efforts, among many other competing priorities, it would not have been possible to prepare this report in the required time frame.

NATIONAL RESEARCH COUNCIL REVIEW

This report has been reviewed in draft form by individuals chosen for their diverse perspectives and technical expertise, in accordance with procedures approved by the NRC's Report Review Committee. The purpose of this independent review is to provide candid and critical comments that will assist the institution in making its published report as sound as possible and to ensure that the report meets institutional standards for objectivity, evidence, and responsiveness to the study charge. The review comments and draft manuscript remain confidential to protect the integrity of the deliberative process.

We wish to thank the following individuals for their review of this report: Philip Auerswald, Harvard University; Robert Carpenter, University of Maryland; Merton Flemings, Massachusetts Institute of Technology; Christina Gabriel, Carnegie Mellon University; Paul Horn, International Business Machines Corporation; Henry Kelly, Federation of American Scientists; Charles Kolb, Aerodyne Research, Inc.; Vernon Ruttan, University of Minnesota; Jeffrey Sohl, University of New Hampshire; and Nicholas Vonortas, George Washington University. Although the reviewers listed above have provided many constructive comments and suggestions, they were not asked to endorse the conclusions or recommendations, nor did they see the final draft of the report before its release. Responsibility for the final content of this report rests entirely with the authoring committee and the institution.

Gerry Dineen has overseen the Academies review process for this report. Appointed by the National Research Council, he was responsible for making certain that an independent examination of this report was carried out in accordance with institutional procedures and that all review comments were carefully considered. This multi-year study has produced 11 volumes, many of which have benefited from Gerry Dinneen's guidance and good counsel. The STEP Board and Project Committee recognizes and are grateful for his contribution.

STRUCTURE OF THE REPORT

Following the Executive Summary listing core findings and recommendations, this volume summarizes the analysis of the Committee in eight sections. This Preface has set out the role of the Committee and the parameters of its work. The Introduction in Part I describes public-private partnerships, the motivation for partnerships, and the varieties of partnerships, and then identifies some core conditions contributing to successful partnerships. Part II contains the Committee's findings and recommendations. Following Part III's overview of the broader environment for innovation, Part IV looks more specifically at U.S. innovation policy, in both retrospect and prospect. It identifies some of the central challenges facing U.S. policy makers in this area. Part V provides an overview of the Committee's review of selected U.S. public-private partnerships. These include a synopsis of the Committee's analysis of the SEMATECH consortium, a summary of the assessments of the Small Business Innovation Research and ATP programs, as well as a précis of the scope and potential of science and technology parks associated with the Ames and Sandia national laboratories. Part VI takes up the issues of accountability and assessment, which the Committee identifies as key factors contributing to successful partnerships. In today's interconnected world, partnerships have to be assessed in a global context; Part VII provides this important perspective. Finally, Part VIII sets out the Committee's conclusions; suggests further directions for analysis; and outlines considerations for policy makers seeking to foster innovation through public-private partnerships.

Gordon Moore **Bill Spencer** **Charles Wessner**

Executive Summary

This summary report reflects the findings and recommendations of a comprehensive program-based review of public-private partnerships. The study was conducted under the auspices of the Board on Science, Technology, and Economic Policy of the National Research Council, with the help of numerous national and international experts. The Committee's analysis has included a significant but necessarily limited portion of the variety of cooperative activity that takes place between the government and the private sector in the United States and abroad.[1] It has focused on "best practices" as a way of drawing out positive guidance for future public policy.

Public-private partnerships, involving cooperative research and development activities among industry, universities, and government laboratories can play an instrumental role in accelerating the development of new technologies from idea to market. Experience shows that partnerships work—thereby contributing to national missions in health, energy, the environment, and national defense—while also contributing to the nation's ability to capitalize on its R&D investments. Properly constructed, operated, and evaluated partnerships can provide an effective means for accelerating the progress of technology from the laboratory to the market.

---

[1]For example, aside from SEMATECH (where DARPA served as the government partner) and broader references to DARPA's role in the development of the Internet, DARPA's programs and contributions have not been specifically reviewed. For an overview of the scope of cooperative activity at the federal and state levels, see C. Coburn and D. Berglund, *Partnerships: A Compendium of State and Federal Cooperative Technology Programs,* Columbus, OH: Battelle Press, 1995; and the RaDiUS database. See <http://www.rand.org/services/radius/>.

Bringing the benefits of new products, new processes, and new knowledge into the market is a key challenge for an innovation system. Partnerships facilitate the transfer of scientific knowledge to real products; they represent one means to improve the output of the U.S. innovation system. Partnerships help by bringing innovations to the point where private actors can introduce them to the market. Accelerated progress in obtaining the benefits of new products, new processes, and new knowledge into the market has positive consequences for economic growth and human welfare. The case of the semiconductor industry illustrates that partnerships have also contributed directly to furthering the global competitiveness of U.S. industry.

Partnerships are diverse in structure, mechanisms, and goals. This is one of their advantages. Partnerships as diverse as the Small Business Innovation Research program (SBIR) program, the Advanced Technology Program (ATP), and SEMATECH have all demonstrated positive results commensurate with their challenges and objectives. Indeed, the partnership concept is wider than a "one size fits all" solution to the challenges of technology development. Flexibility and experimentation are key elements in effective policymaking for public-private partnerships.

Successful partnerships tend to be characterized by industry initiation and leadership, public commitments that are limited and defined, clear objectives, cost sharing, and learning through sustained evaluations of measurable outcomes, as well as the application of the lessons to program operations.[2] At the same time, it is important to recognize that although partnerships are a valuable policy instrument, they are not a panacea; their demonstrated utility does not imply that all partnerships will be successful. Indeed, the high risk—high payoff nature of innovation research and development assures some disappointment.

Partnerships focus on earlier stages of the innovation stream than many venture investments, and often concentrate on technologies that pose greater risks and offer broader returns than the private investor normally finds attractive.[3] Moreover, the limited scale of most partnerships—compared to private institutional investments—and their sunset provisions tend to ensure early recourse to private funding or national procurement. In terms of project scale and timing in the innovation process, public-private partnerships do not displace private finance. Properly constructed research and development partnerships can actually elicit

---

[2]Features associated with more successful partnerships are described in the Introduction to this report.

[3]Some programs also support broadly applicable technologies that, while desirable for society as a whole, are difficult for individual firms to undertake because returns are difficult for individual firms to appropriate. A major example is the Advanced Technology Program.

"crowding in" phenomena with public investments in R&D providing the needed signals to attract private investment.[4]

The Committee's study highlights the need to provide support for basic and applied research across a broad range of disciplines, especially in relatively neglected disciplines such as physics, chemistry, mechanical, and electrical engineering. These disciplines underpin continued advances in information technology, a major source of economic growth. They are also essential for continued progress in health. Capitalizing on the nation's substantial investments in biomedicine requires complementary investments in often seemingly unrelated disciplines supporting information technology.

Partnerships offer a means to integrate the diverse participants in the U.S. innovation system.[5] Partnerships provide an institutional structure with financial and policy incentives within which companies, universities, national laboratories, and research institutes can cooperate to accelerate the development of promising technologies.

Partnerships are also a versatile means of achieving pressing national objectives. In times of national need, such as the current struggle with terrorism, partnerships can be an effective means to accelerate the development of the technologies required to meet new requirements for security in areas such as health and transportation. Partnerships have a demonstrated capability to marshal national expertise from industry, government, and universities to help meet national needs.[6] Programs such as the SBIR and ATP offer proven mechanisms for ad-

---

[4]David, Hall, and Toole survey the econometric evidence over the past 35 years. They note that the "findings overall are ambivalent and the existing literature as a whole is subject to the criticism that the nature of the 'experiment(s)' that the investigators envisage is not adequately specified." It seems that both crowding out and crowding in can occur. The essential finding is that the evidence is inconclusive and that assumptions about crowding out are unsubstantiated. The outcome appears to depend on the specifics of the circumstance, and these are not adequately captured in available data. See Paul A. David, Bronwyn H. Hall, and Andrew A. Toole, "Is Public R&D a Complement or Substitute for Private R&D? A Review of the Econometric Evidence." NBER Working Paper 7373, October 1999. Relatedly, Feldman and Kelley cite the "halo effect" created by ATP awards in helping firms signal their potential to private investors. See Maryann Feldman and Maryellen Kelley, "Leveraging Research and Development: The Impact of the Advanced Technology Program," in National Research Council, *The Advanced Technology Program,* C. Wessner, ed., Washington D.C.: National Academy Press, 2001.

[5]See Richard Nelson, *National Innovation System*, New York: Oxford University Press, 1993.

[6]See National Research Council, *Making the Nation Safer, The Role of Science and Technology in Countering Terrorism,* Washington D.C.: National Academy Press, 2002. This report notes that "for the government and private sector to work together on increasing homeland security, effective public-private partnerships and cooperative projects must occur. There are many models for government-industry collaboration—cooperative research and development agreements, the NIST Advanced Technology Program, and the Small Business Innovative Research program, to cite a few" (p. 359).

vancing the development of new technologies to address national missions.[7] Because they are flexible and can be organized on an *ad hoc* basis, partnerships are an effective means to rapidly focus diverse expertise and innovative technologies to help counter new threats.

[7]The National Institute of Allergies and Infectious Diseases at the National Institutes of Health, for example, has rapidly expanded its efforts in support of research on possible agents of bio-terrorism in response to recent threats and attacks. Specifically, NIAID has expanded research to develop countermeasures—including vaccines, therapeutics, and diagnostic tests—needed to respond and control the release of agents of bio-terrorism. An important tool in this effort has been the SBIR program. See NIAID FY 2003 Budget Justification Narrative at <http://www.niaid.nih.gov/director/congress/2002/cj/>.

I

INTRODUCTION

Introduction

Public-private partnerships involving cooperative research and development among industry, government, and universities can play an instrumental role in introducing key new technologies to the market. Experience shows that partnerships involving government participation in cooperative research and development with industry, universities, and government laboratories can work. They often contribute to national missions in health, energy, the environment, and national defense and to the nation's ability to capitalize on its R&D investments.

This report presents an overview of the work of the National Research Council's Committee on Government-Industry Partnerships for the Development of New Technologies, under the auspices of the Board on Science, Technology, and Economic Policy. In its review of a variety of partnership programs in the United States, the Committee has found that partnerships constitute a vital positive element of public policy, helping to address major challenges and opportunities at the nexus of science, technology, and economic growth.[1]

This chapter introduces some core issues from the Committee's portfolio of work on public-private partnerships. The first section sets out what public-private partnerships are, introduces some situations in which they might help advance the development of new technologies, and identifies some of the forms that they can take. The second section highlights the programs that have been the focus of the Committee's analysis and relates some insights gained from this review. The final section of this introduction provides a user's guide to the Committee's analysis, which is summarized in this report.

[1]See Part II for the Committee's recommendations.

PUBLIC-PRIVATE PARTNERSHIPS

From the early days of the republic, the United States has benefited from effective public-private partnerships. Cooperation between the government and private firms has contributed to the achievement of many national goals from infrastructure construction to weapons development. In the post cold war period, this cooperation expanded to include knowledge generation and technology development through a wide variety of mechanisms.[2] Today's partnerships frequently involve direct support for research and development carried out by private firms, often in cooperation with universities or national laboratories. Partnerships have represented and continue to represent a pragmatic means of achieving national goals and exploiting technological opportunities that benefit the nation.[3]

Drivers of Partnerships

Private investment to develop a new technology can be impeded by factors such as project scale and cost, dispersed expertise, and technical and commercial risk, even if these investments offer the prospect of substantial benefits to the firm, the industry, and to the society as a whole.[4] By helping firms to overcome these barriers to investment, public-private partnerships can contribute to the development of industrial processes, products, and services that might not otherwise emerge spontaneously, and in this way help address government missions and generate greater public welfare.

- Developing new technologies often require collective action, particularly in the case of high-spillover goods, where technology advances generates

---

[2]For a brief history of partnerships in the United States, see Part III of this report.

[3]See David B. Audretsch, Barry Bozeman, Kathryn L. Combs, Maryann Feldman, Albert N. Link, Donald S. Siegel, Paula Stephan, Gregory Tassey, and Charles Wessner, "The Economics of Science and Technology," in *Journal of Technology Transfer*, 27, 2002, p. 155-203. The authors note that "'public/private partnerships' have evolved from governments' desire to steer private investment towards certain types of scientific activity and the development and use of new technologies. Thus, the federal government has attempted to establish an environment that is conducive for private sector investment in research and development (R&D), as well as one in which the public and private sectors can be partners in undertaking innovative activity" (p. 156).

[4]The Committee's study of Government-Industry Partnerships suggests that public-private partnerships can provide a practical response to meet national challenges. The study of the Advanced Technology Program (ATP) notes, for example, that ATP was "initiated as a means of funding high-risk R&D with broad commercial and societal benefits that would not be undertaken by a single company, either because the risk was too high or because a large enough share of the benefits of success would not accrue to the company for it to make the investment." See National Research Council, *The Advanced Technology Program: Assessing Outcomes,* Charles W. Wessner, ed., Washington, D.C.: National Academy Press, 2001, p. 39.

benefits beyond those that can be captured by innovating firms. Partnerships can be a means of encouraging the cooperation necessary for socially valuable innovation.[5]

- New technologies often involve investments in combinations of technologies that may remain unexploited (or silo) in companies or industries. Joint research activities can facilitate the cooperation necessary to achieve the commercial potential of these technologies.
- Partnerships encourage firms to undertake socially beneficial R&D. The return on R&D investment, even for promising technologies, can be perceived to be too low when firms heavily discount distant income streams or when risks related to technical development and commercialization are seen as substantial.
- Firms may not invest in R&D when they do not expect to be able to capture enough of the revenue from the resulting innovations. This occurs when the potential market for the company's new technology is broader than the firm can secure. Reduced R&D investments by private firms can also occur when they find it difficult to assign or enforce intellectual property rights, lowering expectations for returns on investments.
- Each of these factors can affect firms' internal "hurdle rates" with regard to investments in new products or processes that may be beneficial to many firms or the economy as a whole.[6]

Partnerships are also a versatile means of achieving pressing national objectives—a point discussed further below. In times of national need, such as the current struggle with terrorism, partnerships can be an effective means to accelerate the development of the technologies required to meet the multifaceted challenges of national security. As a recent Academy report observed,[7]

---

[5]Technological knowledge is considered by many to be peculiar in that it is inherently "slippery"—that is, it can be replicated and transmitted at very low marginal cost. If its generation contributes a positive externality to society, the gross social benefit of R&D activity can exceed private benefit. Neoclassical theory argues that in such cases R&D activity is likely to be undersupplied relative to some social optimum. See Richard N. Langlois and Paul L. Robertson, "Stop Crying over Spilt Knowledge: A Critical Look at the Theory of Spillovers and Technical Change." Paper prepared for the MERIT Conference on Innovation, Evolution, and Technology, August 25-27, 1996, Maastricht, Netherlands. The authors analyze the idea of knowledge spillovers, noting that the processes are more complex and context dependant than portrayed in the neoclassical literature.

[6]See Albert N. Link, "Enhanced R&D Efficiency in an ATP-funded Joint Venture," in *The Advanced Technology Program, Assessing Outcome, op.cit.* For a review of why firms might underinvest in R&D, see Albert N. Link, "Public/Private Partnerships as a Tool to Support Industrial R&D: Experiences in the United States," Final Report to the Working Group on Innovation and Technology Policy of the OECD Committee for Scientific and Technology Policy, January 1999.

[7]National Research Council, *Making the Nation Safer: The Role of Science and Technology in Countering Terrorism,* Washington, D.C.: National Academy Press, 2002.

For the United States to take advantage of the significant scientific and technical expertise residing in the private sector, and to overcome the market disincentive for single firms to invest in improving their security, the federal government must explore creative and flexible ways to motivate and to develop and adopt counter-terrorism technologies.

For the government and private sector to work together on increasing homeland security, effective public-private partnerships and cooperative projects must occur. There are many models for government-industry collaboration—cooperative research and development agreements, the NIST Advanced Technology Program, and the Small Business Innovative Research program to cite a few.

Varieties of Partnerships

In the United States, the advancement of new technologies in support of national missions or the generation of welfare-enhancing products or processes has often been pursued through a wide range of public-private partnerships.[8] The proliferation of these programs and the diversity of their structures and goals underscore the need for a better understanding of the conditions contributing to their success. This study of public-private cooperation has focused on three types of partnerships. These are:

- **Industry consortia:** In an R&D consortium a certain portion and type of a participating company's R&D is funneled into a separate organization where it is carried out collectively and where the research results are shared among the member firms. Consortia are particularly useful in the case of high-spillover technologies, where each firm may be reluctant to contribute to the production of goods that by their nature become widely available to others at little or no cost. In a consortium, firms can lower R&D costs or increase R&D efficiency while continuing to compete privately through their own product-related R&D programs. The role for government in the case of industry consortia is to legally enable this cooperation and when appropriate contribute funding and/or re-

[8]An illustrative list here could include partnerships in such sectors as electronic storage, flat-panel displays, turbine technologies, new textile manufacturing techniques, new materials, magnetic storage, next-generation vehicles, batteries, biotechnology, optoelectronics, and ship construction. For example, the Partnership for a New Generation of Vehicles (PNGV) is a cooperative R&D program between the federal government and the U.S. Council for Automotive Research, whose members are Daimler Chrysler, Ford Motor Company, and General Motors. Its purpose is to develop a new generation of automobiles with up to three times the fuel economy of a 1993 mid-size automobile. Seven annual reviews of the technical developments related to PNGV have so far been undertaken. Most recently, see National Research Council, *Review of the Research Program of the Partnership for a New Generation of Vehicles: Seventh Report,* Washington, D.C.: National Academy Press, 2001.

search facilities (e.g., national laboratories) to advance research on technologies of mutual interest.[9]

- **Innovation funding:** Small businesses often face major constraints in bringing innovations to market. Financial markets often operate under conditions of imperfect information, often to the disadvantage of small firms working on less routine, more innovative projects. Small firms may also decide not to develop an innovation if they are not able to capture enough of the pay-off from this work—the so-called appropriability problem. Imperfections in capital markets can sometimes pose major challenges to small firms trying to bring their innovations to market. Federal partnerships such as the Small Business Innovation Research program (SBIR) and the Advanced Technology Program (ATP) provide awards that can help to address the early-stage funding requirements faced by firms engaged in the innovation-to-market process.
- **Laboratory-based science and technology clusters:** Promoting innovation-led growth by encouraging knowledge clusters around the nucleus of national laboratories and research facilities is an important aspect of public-private partnerships in the United States. Traditional S&T parks are expected to diffuse knowledge and technology and thus provide an engine of growth for a region. In practice, however, the goals of these Science and Technology parks are often extensive, with imperfect definitions, and achievement can be correspondingly difficult to assess. The review of the Sandia S&T Park and the Ames S&T Park stresses the importance of clearly articulated goals and frequent assessment.

OVERALL LESSONS ABOUT PARTNERSHIPS

The Committee's Focus and Approach

Numerous public-private partnerships at the federal, state, and local levels are underway in the United States; one compendium, from the mid-1990s, listing partnerships in the United States is itself over 600 pages long.[10] At the same time, public debate about partnerships has tended to be long on rhetoric and short on practical analysis. Addressing this point, Berglund and Coburn note that "the debate should address not whether these [partnership] programs will endure, but whether they are shaped properly—at the program and aggregate levels—to achieve

[9]The National Cooperative Research Act (NCRA) in 1984 revised existing antitrust laws and penalties were seen to be too restrictive, possibly impeding the ability of U.S. companies to compete in global markets. This act encouraged U.S. firms to collaborate on generic, pre-competitive research.

[10]See Dan Berglund and Christopher Coburn, *Partnerships, A Compendium of State and Federal Cooperative Technology Programs,* Columbus, OH: Battelle Press, 1995.

the desired benefits."[11] Reflecting this viewpoint, the Committee decided not to conduct a necessarily broad review of all these cooperative activities. Instead, it elected to carry out in-depth studies of selected partnerships that are particularly illustrative of the pubic policy issues related to technology partnerships.

Notably, the Committee has focused on:

- The Small Business Innovation Research (SBIR) program, the largest U.S. partnership program, currently funded at approximately $1.3 billion per year across 10 government agencies;
- The Advanced Technology Program (ATP), which was one of the most politically controversial and yet is also recognized as one of the most effective of the major innovation funding partnership programs today[12];
- SEMATECH, arguably one of the most prominent U.S. partnerships;
- The Ames and Sandia S&T Parks, which are representative examples of positive interactions between national laboratories and local communities interested in the development and/or the exploitation of technology clusters; and
- The Committee also focused on the growing need for new resources for research in areas related to information technology, and for greater cooperation in responding to emerging needs and strategic opportunities in biotechnology and information technology. Many see enhanced cooperation and reinforced research in disciplines related to information technology as fundamental to sustaining the positive technology-based growth that has recently characterized the U.S. economy.

To meet its objective of policy-relevant analysis the Committee has focused additionally on positive lessons or "best practices," rather than the experiences of less successful partnerships, although it is certainly true that much can be learned from failures as well as successes.[13] This selective focus has enabled the Com-

[11] *Ibid.*

[12] The controversy surrounding this program has receded. In a recent report, Secretary of Commerce, Donald Evans, broadly endorsed the program, albeit with recommendations for some changes in its operation. The debate is now more traditional, focusing on levels of funding and rates of expenditure rather than on the program itself. In a recent report, the Senate also endorsed the program, remarking that it had been subject to a large number of assessments by different organizations, including the study by the Academies. See National Research Council, *The Advanced Technology Program: Assessing Outcomes*, *op.cit.*; Senate Appropriations Committee Report 107-47; Department of Commerce, *The Advanced Technology Program: Reform With a Purpose*, Washington, D.C., February 2002.

[13] In one case the Committee did commission an analysis of lessons that might be learned from comparing the experience of a less successful and a successful partnership, see John B. Horrigan, "Cooperating Competitors: A Comparison of MCC and SEMATECH." Monograph, Washington, D.C.: National Research Council, 1999.

mittee to identify more clearly some of the characteristics of successful partnerships. The Committee has also enhanced the value of its work—and affirmed its relevance—by responding to a series of requests from Congress and the Executive Branch for careful, objective analyses of current partnerships.[14]

Conditions for Successful Partnerships

To be effective, partnerships as venues for joint R&D activities require that several of the multiple actors—entrepreneurs, firms, government agencies, and non-profit organizations—be able to work together productively. The innovation environment for partnerships conditions and shapes their performance.

The federal government policies also collectively shape the larger environment in which innovation takes place. For example, federal policies affecting capital formation and corporate governance play important roles in competitive performance.[15] The range and diversity of these policies are substantial. They include government policies related to taxation, especially capital gains; fiscal and monetary matters; education and training; trade promotion and expansion; regulatory policies (e.g., for anti-trust and the environment), intellectual property protection, government procurement, and export control.[16] These policies can all directly affect the process of innovation, sometimes decisively.[17]

At an operational level, the organizational features of the partnership clearly matter. Although partnerships vary in scale, mission, and scope, successful partnerships appear to share some similar broad characteristics. These include: [18]

- **The Value of Industry Leadership:** Industry leadership provides partnerships with technical expertise, experienced management, and proven flexibility while also enhancing the consortium's credibility with its mem-

---

[14]These requests are noted in the Preface.

[15]See National Research Council, *U.S. Industry in 2000: Studies in Competitive Performance*, Washington, D.C.: National Academy Press, 1999, p. 5.

[16]See, for example, the observations of Ed Zchau, a member of Congress in the 1980s from Silicon Valley, in his article, "Government Policies for Innovation and Growth" in National Research Council, *The Positive Sum Strategy, Harnessing Technology for Economic Growth,* Washington, D.C.: National Academy Press, 1986, pp. 535-39.

[17]We are indebted to Ralph Landau for this and related observations. For example, intellectual property protection plays a key role in the continued development of the biotechnology industry. See Wesley M. Cohen and John Walsh, "Public Research, Patents and Implications for Industrial R&D in the Drug, Biotechnology, Semiconductor and Computer Industries" in National Research Council, *U.S. Industry in 2000: Studies in Competitive Performance, op. cit.*, pp. 4-5. The interaction of supportive technology policies and restrictive trade policies proved effective in some countries in the 1970s and 1980s. See Daniel I. Okimoto, *Between MITI and the Market: Japanese Industrial Policy for High Technology*, Stanford, California: Stanford University Press, 1989.

[18]These factors are interrelated. They are listed separately to improve analytical clarity.

bers and the policy community. The experience of the SEMATECH consortium underscores the need[19] for the commitment of senior management of the participating firms in a consortium. Their active participation on the SEMATECH Board and their assignment of top-quality staff were essential for the full benefit of government support for the consortium to be realized. Effective leadership of a multi-firm consortium is an asset in resolving differences among consortium participants over competing objectives. Strong links to members enhance the consortium's legitimacy when redirecting the research program and establishing objectives and metrics for project performance. Effective public leadership is also an asset in conveying the message of the consortium to the government and to other interested parties. For government programs that fund innovation, identifying effective management teams is an important part of the grant and evaluation procedures. Effective leadership in the management of S&T parks, such as those at Sandia and Ames, has proven essential for the benefits of relationships between the national laboratory and nearby firms to be realized.

- **The Importance of Roadmaps:** The Committee's recognition of the importance of technology roadmaps draws from SEMATECH's experience, where the industry perceived early on that problems of coordination could arise with a complex technology, multiple participants, and many ways of proceeding. This realization led to cooperative efforts with the Semiconductor Industry Association (SIA), the Semiconductor Research Corporation (SRC), and other parties to develop a technology roadmap setting out the relationships among science, technology, and applications as a point of reference for the researchers, technologists, project managers, suppliers, and users involved in and affected by the consortium's work. As a general approach, roadmaps can advance similar coordination functions in other industry partnerships and in this way contribute to more efficient and more cooperative research.[20]

---

[19]Specifics relating to the circumstances faced by firms in the semiconductor industry at the time of SEMATECH's birth and consequent development will differ, of course, from the realities faced by other industry consortia. While not all details of SEMATECH's experience can be generalized, broader lessons can be drawn from its largely positive experience, but much depends on the particular circumstances of a given partnership.

[20]The Roadmap, now the International Roadmap for Semiconductors, continues to be a central focus of research activity at what is now International SEMATECH (ISMT). In addition to its close cooperation with SEMI, the equipment and suppliers consortium, ISMT maintains cooperative activities with other consortia in Europe (IMEC) and information exchanges with Japan's SELETE program in an effort to stay on the industry's exceptional productivity curve, which has resulted in a 25 percent cost per function decrease each year. See *International SEMATECH Annual Report 2001*, at <www.sematech.org>.

- **The Significance of Shared Commitment and Costs:** Success in a cooperative partnership depends on each of the participants acting in ways that advance the joint objectives of the partnership. This motivation can be enhanced if the participant makes a commitment in funds or other resources to the partnership. Consortia work best when there are clear gains through participation or increased costs when cooperation is reduced. Having a sizeable stake in the outcome of the partnership enhances the motivation of those involved to make the partnership succeed; similarly, private contributions to consortia also provide a powerful incentive to terminate efforts that are not meeting objectives.[21] In the case of early-stage innovation funding, individual entrepreneurs are motivated to qualify for awards in order to reap, ultimately, the financial rewards of a marketable technology. The government's goal is to leverage the motivation of the marketplace to meet government objectives.[22] These objectives include accelerating the development of new products to improve health with new medical products, aid the environment with new energy sources, enhance national defense with better communications, and to strengthen international competitiveness of national industries, such as textiles, automobiles, batteries, and electronics.
- **The Vital Role of Assessment:** The inclusion of an appropriate and ongoing assessment program is an integral part of the organization of a well-constructed partnership. The measurement of success in turn requires a clear articulation of a partnership's goals and desired outcomes. As the Committee's study of the Ames and Sandia S&T parks shows, the goals of partnerships vary, along with the standards by which we are to gauge their success. The assessment process of the Advanced Technology Program is in many respects a model, because it incorporates a rigorous competitive selection process with an independent evaluation of the project's technical and commercial merit, as well as its potential for broad-based economic benefits. Importantly, the ATP awards are regularly followed and rigorously assessed. As the results of the assessment activity are integrated more into the operations of the program the knowledge generated can help the partnerships adapt in ways that foster better results.

  The multiple assessments undertaken by this study have contributed to the literature on partnerships, first by the application of a variety of economic assessment methods to partnership activity and, second, by gathering a great deal of tacit knowledge about various programs, including their goals, metrics, mode of operation, and current challenges.

---

[21]This is the case with the matching requirement of the ATP, a provision further buttressed by the program's regular assessment and review.

[22]The SBIR program may best exemplify this approach.

As reflected in Table 1, the characteristics of successful partnerships tend to be complementary in furthering partnership performance.[23]

TABLE 1 Structuring Incentives Within the Context of a Partnership

Strategy / *Objective*	**Improving Motivation**	**Improving Knowledge**
Improving Coordination	Effective Leadership	Agreement, Roadmaps, Goals & Metrics of Progress
Improving Cooperation	Shared Costs & Shared Stakes in Outcome	Regular Evaluation, & Member Feedback

A GUIDE TO THIS REPORT

Public-private partnerships are increasingly recognized as an important, sometimes critical policy component of technology-based growth, affecting both the process of innovation and the pace of technology development.[24] This report presents a summary of the Committee's analysis, which has included a significant but necessarily limited portion of the variety of cooperative activity that takes place between the government and the private sector. The Committee's desire to carry out an analysis of current partnerships that is directly relevant to contemporary policy making has conditioned the selection of the specific programs reviewed.

Part III of this report notes that a growing body of economic thought—often articulated in terms of New Growth Theory—which argues that the composition

[23]The four factors identified by the Committee as bearing on the success of partnerships find analytical support in the New Institutional Economics literature. This literature addresses problems of collective action governing activities involving jointly produced outcomes. Partnerships are a prime example of collective action. To be successful, partnerships need to help participants overcome incentive problems related to motivation and information asymmetries that condition the cooperation and coordination necessary for successful outcomes. See Donald E. Campbell, *Incentives: Motivations and the Economics of Information,* Cambridge, UK: Cambridge University Press, 1995. See also, Mancur Olson, *The Logic of Collective Action*, Cambridge, MA: Harvard University Press, 1965. Finally, see Elinor Ostrom, "A Behavioral Approach to the Rational Choice Theory of Collective Action," *American Political Science Review* 92 (1) 1998.

[24]See National Research Council, *Funding a Revolution; Government Support for Computing Research*, Washington, D.C.: National Academy Press, 1999. This report documents the substantial investments in information technologies, including platform technologies such as the Internet. The report also notes the difficulty many have in recognizing the scale and effectiveness of public contributions to the innovation process.

of the economy matters and that high technology industries in particular bring special benefits to regional and national economies.[25]

Part IV of this report points to the breadth, diversity, and significance of public support for technological innovation, knowledge generation, and infrastructure development in the United States. It provides a brief historical overview of federal support for new technologies and new products. It shows that federal public-private partnerships have served the nation throughout its history by accelerating innovation and enhancing national security. Partnerships have contributed to improvements in agricultural productivity, major infrastructure development, and the development of new enabling technologies. Federally supported partnerships have thus helped the nation respond to a variety of national missions, stretching from before the Civil War (the telegraph) to the Cold War (semiconductors and computers) to today's struggle with terrorism (vaccines). Indeed, while the U.S. economy has and continues to be distinguished by the extent to which individual researchers and entrepreneurs take the lead in developing innovations and starting new businesses, they have frequently acted in conjunction with public investments. America's entrepreneurs often harvest crops sown on fields made more fertile by the government's long-term investments in research and development.

Maintaining national capacities for science-based growth (i.e., keeping these fields fertile through sustained investments in basic research across a broad range of disciplines) is therefore a key policy concern. As noted in Part IV it is normal that the federal research portfolio should evolve in response to new scientific opportunities and shifting national needs. Reallocations with respect to individual agency budget priorities, however, have led to unplanned declines in federal support for the disciplines underpinning information technologies. These declines have potentially significant negative ramifications for future economic growth.

The impact of changes in the distribution of support across disciplines is all the more significant given that the frontiers of knowledge are increasingly interdisciplinary. As Marvin Cassman of the National Institutes of Health points out, biology and the biotechnology industries are today confronted with more information than they can assimilate. Biologists really have no alternative but to draw on tools from chemical engineering, physics, and computer science in order to construct a quantitative dynamic structure for biological systems.[26] This demands that support for research, even in priority areas, be based more broadly. To over-

[25]This view is held by policymakers around the world. For an informed perspective, see Richard R. Nelson, The *Sources of Economic Growth*, Cambridge, MA: Harvard University Press, 2000. See Box A of this report for additional citations and discussion of the various facets of the New Growth Theory as it applies to partnerships. Also see Michael Porter, *Clusters of Innovation: Regional Foundations of Competitiveness*, Washington, D.C.: Council on Competitiveness, 2001.

[26]See Marvin Cassman, "Exploiting the Biotechnology Revolution: Training and Tools," in National Research Council, *Capitalizing on New Needs and New Opportunities: Government-Industry Partnerships in Biotechnology and Information Technologies*, C. Wessner, ed., Washington, D.C.: National Academy Press, 2002, p. 134.

come the intellectual and disciplinary biases that hinder interdisciplinary collaboration, government funding for "glue grants" for new disciplines such as bioinformatics and for computational research should be expanded. [27]

The Committee's work has highlighted also the "best practices" lessons from the SEMATECH consortium. Leading industrialists and expert economists in the United States and abroad see the consortium as having contributed to the resurgence of the U.S. semiconductor industry to its current position.[28] Acting on this perception, governments around the world have launched numerous national and regional partnership programs, each providing substantial support for research and pre-competitive product development to national or regional semiconductor industries.

In light of these efforts and the genuine technical challenges facing the industry, continued United States leadership in the semiconductor industry cannot be taken for granted.[29] The decrease in support for basic research in the disciplines that underpin the growth of the U.S. economy should be reversed. Indeed, renewed cooperation among firms, laboratories, and universities is likely to prove essential to maintaining the health and vitality of the industry.

> As illustrated above, partnerships can represent a pragmatic response for firms and government agencies unable to independently and efficiently undertake needed investments. One goal of partnerships is thus to encourage the development of industrial processes, products, and services that firms cannot carry out alone and in this way develop new knowledge to apply to government missions in health, environmental protection, and national security.

Lastly, given that they can be formed as necessary to draw together dispersed talents and capacities across the nation, partnerships can be an effective tool to address urgent national missions, such as the new war on terror.

---

[27]See Recommendations in National Research Council, *Capitalizing on New Needs and New Opportunities, op. cit.*, p. 67.

[28]See National Research Council, *Conflict and Cooperation in National Competition for High Technology Industry*. Washington, D.C.: National Academy Press, 1996, and as part of this series, National Research Council, *Securing the Future: Regional and National Programs to Support the Semiconductor Industry, op. cit.* (forthcoming).

[29]See Jeffrey T. Macher, David C. Mowery, and David A. Hodges, "Semiconductors," *U.S. Industry in 2000: Studies in Competitive Performance*, David C. Mowery, ed., Washington, D.C.: National Academy Press, 1999.

Part V turns to the Committee's extensive work in reviewing three types of public-private partnerships in the United States: consortia, innovation funding, and laboratory-based science and technology clusters. As noted above, the Committee analyzed the challenges facing the global semiconductor industry, explored the contributions of consortia, and documented the expansion of national and regional programs to support this industry. The Committee also convened leading experts from industry and academia to review the prospects and potential of a solid-state lighting consortium. A properly constructed consortium could accelerate technological progress, rendering this new technology more versatile, more economical, and therefore more acceptable to consumers. The widespread use of solid-state lighting technologies might yield substantial energy savings and reduce the environmental impact of power generation.

The reviews of the Small Business Innovation Research Program (SBIR) and the Advanced Technology Program (ATP) highlight specific issues related to assessing the performance of public-private partnerships for which the federal government provides awards to small firms to help overcome early-stage financing hurdles or to facilitate the development by large and small firms of a promising technology or product. ATP and SBIR complement each other and address different points in the innovation process. Because proposals are developed by private companies, the ATP selection process is essentially industry-driven. ATP funds are matched by awardees and are directed to pre-commercial research rather than product development. SBIR awards are smaller and are intended to develop the scientific and technical merit of research ideas in order to facilitate their commercialization and meet the federal agency goals.[30]

The Committee's examination of S&T parks focuses attention on the availability of funding over sustained periods, the presence and willingness of individuals and teams in the private sector to commercialize some of the knowledge generated, availability of physical infrastructure and quality-of-life amenities, and the need for effective leadership to facilitate and guide park development. The goals of the parks themselves, however, often vary substantially. The Sandia

[30]To provide for an objective assessment of the SBIR program, a part of the program's recent reauthorization, the Congress tasked the National Research Council with a multi-year, multi-agency review of the SBIR program at the five agencies. See HR5667, Section 108. While complementary, it should be emphasized that the ATP and SBIR programs are different, targeting different points in the innovation process. In terms of rigorous and regular assessment the ATP effort is of high quality. The ATP has also been the subject of an extraordinary amount of outside review and analysis, the most comprehensive being the Committee's own analysis. See National Research Council, *The Advanced Technology Program: Assessing Outcomes, op. cit.* Objective external assessment of SBIR is much more limited, aside from the commendable efforts of the Department of Defense, which reviewed its program and designed innovations to encourage greater commercialization. The National Research Council review of the DoD SBIR program was broadly positive. See National Research Council, *The Small Business Innovation Research Program: An Assessment of the Department of Defense Fast Track Initiative,* C. Wessner, ed., Washington, D.C.: National Academy Press, 2000.

S&T Park is designed to encourage cooperation between Sandia National Laboratories and the private sector on common technical challenges and to contribute to regional development. By contrast, the Ames S&T Park is intended to draw in expertise from Silicon Valley to help NASA achieve its missions. Effective assessment of these parks has to reflect their particular goals. This requires well-defined objectives and metrics early in the parks' development.

Part VI emphasizes that assessments can not only improve the operations of a partnership but can also help to inform the public and policy makers of the risks and benefits from this type of cooperation. Regular assessments of public-private partnerships can also help to ensure the continued technical viability of funded projects and maintain the relevance of the research—thereby facilitating the innovation process.

Finally, Part VII places U.S. public-private partnerships in a global context. It notes that while the competition in high-technology industries is not new, it does seem to be accelerating as new entrants put in more resources, often in new or expanded partnerships.[31] The belief in many nations that the government should support new technologies or industries considered strategic or simply important to the national economy is accelerating interest in partnerships as effective policy tools for encouraging innovation. The terms and nature of this aid vary greatly across countries, but in supporting their high-technology industries, many governments are looking to models of success arising out of partnership experiments in the United States. SEMATECH in particular has inspired similar ventures in Japan, Europe, and in the newly industrializing countries of East Asia. In addition, there is increasing interest in the structure, goals, and evaluations of program awards aimed at commercializing university inventions. Interest in award programs such as ATP and SBIR, is particularly strong among European governments, research institutes, and such international organizations as the Organisation for Economic Cooperation and Development.

• • •

This review of past, current, and potential partnerships is intended to advance public understanding of the nature and potential of partnerships. By helping to bring the benefits of science to the marketplace, partnerships can play a vital role in realizing national missions, encouraging economic growth, and enhancing the well-being of the American people.

---

[31]See Thomas R. Howell, "Competing Programs: Government Support for Microelectronics," in National Research Council, *Securing the Future: Regional and National Programs to Support the Semiconductor Industry,* C. Wessner, ed., Washington, D.C.: National Academy Press, Forthcoming.

II

FINDINGS AND RECOMMENDATIONS

Findings and Recommendations

SUMMARY OF FINDINGS

I. Public-private partnerships, involving cooperative research and development activities among industry, government laboratories, and universities, can play an instrumental role in accelerating the development of new technologies from idea to market.

a. Applications of new biomedical and information technologies, for example, hold the potential for tremendous advances in the health and productivity of Americans. Bringing the results of research to the market—that is, from ideas to innovations to commercial products—is a genuine challenge. Partnerships can be a valuable mechanism to facilitate this process. The nature of partnerships and their potential role in fostering and sustaining improvements in national security, social welfare, and economic growth are, therefore, issues of central policy concern.

b. Experience shows that partnerships involving government participation in cooperative research and development among industry, universities, and government laboratories can work. They often contribute to national missions in health, energy, the environment, and national defense and to the nation's ability to capitalize on its R&D investments.

c. Partnerships help bring innovations to the point where private actors can bring them to the market. Accelerated progress in bringing the benefits of new products, new processes, and new knowledge to the market has positive consequences for economic growth and human welfare.

II. Partnerships offer a means to integrate the diverse participants in the U.S. innovation system.[1]

a. Bringing the benefits of new products, new processes, and new knowledge to the market is a key challenge for an innovation system. Partnerships contribute to our ability to facilitate the transfer of scientific knowledge to real products; they represent one means to improve the output of the U.S. innovation system. Because modern scientific advances hold tremendously positive prospects for humanity, learning how best to facilitate science-based growth is a central challenge for policy makers as we begin the new century. Early progress in, for example, disease detection, prevention, or treatment has direct consequences in terms of human welfare and healthcare costs.

b. Partnerships provide an institutional structure with financial and policy incentives within which companies, universities, national laboratories, and research institutes can cooperate to accelerate the development of promising technologies.

c. In many cases, no single participant could pursue the development of these technologies effectively. The diversity of U.S. partnerships provides a significant advantage to the innovation process in the United States. At the same time, cooperation among firms, universities, and government laboratories is often needed to harness complementary expertise and to realize new synergies. Blending these strengths in a case-by-case fashion is one of the great strengths of partnerships.

III. Partnerships are diverse in structure, mechanisms, and goals. This is one of their advantages. Successful partnerships do tend to be characterized by industry leadership, public commitments that are limited and defined, clear objectives, cost sharing, and effective evaluation processes.

a. Partnership structures, as diverse as the SBIR program, the Advanced Technology Program, and SEMATECH, demonstrate that partnerships, if properly structured, can yield positive results commensurate with their objectives and challenges. Flexibility, experimentation, and learning are key elements in effective policy for partnerships.

b. Features common to successful partnerships include industry initiation and leadership of projects, cost sharing predictable limits to public commitments of resources,[2] clear objectives, and learning through evaluation of measurable outcomes. Effective leadership and cost sharing can help motivate participants in a partnership to act in ways that advance their

---

[1]See Richard Nelson, *National Innovation System*, New York: Oxford University Press, 1993.

[2]Open-ended public funding has the potential to create negative incentive effects. Kornai in this regard explores the implications of "soft budget constraints." See Janos Kornai, *Economics of Shortage*, Amsterdam: North Holland, 1980.

joint objectives. Agreement on goals and metrics of progress, the development of roadmaps, and regular evaluations helps sustain joint effort; taken together, these features contribute to the success of partnerships.[3]

c. Although partnerships are a valuable policy instrument, they are not a panacea; their demonstrated utility does not imply that all partnerships will be successful. Indeed, the high risk – high payoff nature of innovation research and development assures some disappointments.

IV. In terms of both project scale and timing in the innovation process, properly constructed partnerships do not displace private finance.

a. Entrepreneurs sometimes face challenges in attracting the private financing necessary to develop new technologies for the market. While the U.S. venture capital industry is well developed and often plays a key role in the innovation process, it does not provide early stage equity funding for some innovations.[4] In fact, current trends in the venture industry—particularly the increase in deal size—may make certain types of small, early-stage financing less likely, despite the overall increase in venture funding.[5]

b. Partnerships focus on earlier stages of the innovation stream than many venture investments and often concentrate on technologies that pose greater risks and offer broader returns than the private investor will normally find attractive.[6] Public-private partnerships are a mechanism to provide catalytic funding. They articulate needs, sometimes create early demand, and coordinate the needed expertise. In doing so, they help foster the creativity and invention needed to prime the process of innovation.[7] Moreover, the limited scale of most partnerships—compared

---

[3]Features associated with more successful partnerships are described in greater detail in the Introduction to this report.

[4]See Lewis Branscomb and Philip Auerswald, *Taking Technical Risk: How Innovators, Executives, and Investors Manage High-Tech Risks,* Cambridge, MA: MIT Press, 2001. See also Lewis Branscomb, Testimony before Hearing of the Technology Subcommittee of the House Science Committee on the Advanced Technology Program at NIST/DOC, June 14, 2001 at <http://www.house.gov/science/ets/jun14/branscomb.htm>.

[5]Venture capital funding has fallen off sharply from 1999 highs but overall fund size has increased substantially. This means that venture capital investments have recently been larger but fewer. For a broad overview of the early-stage equity market for high-growth ventures in the U.S., see Jeffrey Sohl, "The Early-Stage Equity Market in the USA," *Venture Capital* 1(2):101-120, 1999.

[6]Some programs also support broadly applicable technologies that, while desirable for society as a whole, are difficult for individual firms to undertake because returns are difficult for individual firms to appropriate. A major example is the Advanced Technology Program.

[7]Joseph Schumpeter articulated the role of the entrepreneur—to seize these basic inventions and transform them into economic innovations. See Joseph A. Schumpeter, *Capitalism, Socialism, and Democracy*, New York: Harper and Brothers, 1942. See also William H. Middendorf, *What Every Engineer Should Know About Inventing*, New York and Basel: Marcel Dekker, Inc. 1981.

to private institutional investments—and their sunset provisions tend to ensure early recourse to private funding or national procurement.

c. Concerns about the crowding out of private capital by public funds may be overstated. Properly constructed public-private R&D partnerships can actually elicit "crowding in" phenomena with public R&D investments providing the needed signals to attract private R&D investment.[8]

V. The allocation of federal funding among fields of research has shifted sharply in the last decade with important implications for the future advance of information technology and its contributions to our ability to capitalize on existing and future investments in biomedicine.

a. While among the most efficient in the world, the U.S. innovation system has seen considerable adjustment following the transformations in national priorities brought about by the end of the Cold War and more recently since the onset of the new war on terror.[9] One impact of this adjustment and efforts in the mid-1990s to balance the federal budget has been that the R&D budgets of most federal agencies were reduced in real terms in the 1993-1997 period.[10] When individual agencies cut research programs because of their own mission realignments, the collective impact on the federal investment research portfolio was not anticipated.[11]

---

[8]David, Hall, and Toole survey the econometric evidence on "crowding out" over the past 35 years. They note that the "findings overall are ambivalent and the existing literature as a whole is subject to the criticism that the nature of the "experiment(s)" that the investigators envisage is not adequately specified." It seems that both crowding out and crowding in can occur. The essential finding is that the evidence is inconclusive and that assumptions about crowding out are unsubstantiated. The outcome appears to depend on the specifics of the circumstance, and these are not adequately captured in available data. See Paul A. David, Bronwyn H. Hall, and Andrew A. Toole, "Is Public R&D a Complement or Substitute for Private R&D? A Review of the Econometric Evidence." NBER Working Paper 7373, October 1999. Relatedly, Feldman and Kelley cite the "halo effect" created by ATP awards in helping firms signal their potential to private investors. See Maryann Feldman and Maryellen Kelley, "Leveraging Research and Development: The Impact of the Advanced Technology Program," in National Research Council, *The Advanced Technology Program,* C. Wessner, ed., Washington, D.C.: National Academy Press, 2001.

[9]See David Mowery and Nathan Rosenberg, *Technology and the Pursuit of Economic Growth,* Cambridge: Cambridge University Press, 1989.

[10]The National Institutes of Health is a notable exception, benefiting from substantial real growth in this period. See National Research Council, *Capitalizing on New Needs and New Opportunities—Government-Industry Partnerships in Biotechnology and Information Technologies,* C. Wessner, ed., Washington, D.C.: National Academy Press, 2002

[11]For example, The Department of Defense—the agency with the steepest reductions in R&D (more than 25 percent)—increased funding of oceanographic research and held funding of research in computer science constant. At the same time, research expenditures in other fields, e.g. physics, were reduced very substantially. For a more detailed analysis, see Michael McGeary, "Recent Trends in Federal Funding of Research and Development Related to Health and Information Technology" in *Capitalizing on New Needs and New Opportunities, Government-Industry Partnerships in Biotechnology and Information Technologies, op cit.* See also National Research Council, *Trends in Federal Support of Research and Graduate Education*, S. Merrill, ed., Washington, D.C.: National Academy Press, 2001.

b. As a result of these changes, financial support for such disciplines, as physics, chemistry, and engineering has fallen in real terms over several years. The substantial reductions in support for these disciplines are a source of concern because they underpin the future development of the information technology sector. These reductions did not emerge as the result of a national debate on R&D priorities and the lag effects of these cuts may have unforeseen, long-term consequences.

c. Meanwhile, in response to new needs, new opportunities, and recently, new threats, there has been an expansion in the allocation of U.S. federal research investments toward the health and medical sciences sector. This increase in support for medical research is welcome.[12] It is normal that the federal research portfolio should evolve over time in response to new scientific needs and opportunities.[13] However, the real reductions in support that have occurred over a sustained period (1993-1999) for disciplines that underpin the information technology sector are a cause for concern.

d. It is equally important to recognize that the information and biotechnology sectors—each very important to the nation's economy, security, and well-being—are increasingly interrelated. Advance in one area is often dependant on progress in the other; sectors like the life sciences increasingly rely on parallel advances in information technology for their own advancement. For example, reaping the benefits of sequencing the human genome depends on processing and making sense of enormous amounts of data that in turn will be made possible by advances in computing and networking technologies. Capitalizing on the nation's substantial investments in biomedicine therefore requires complementary investments to advance the fields of science and engineering supporting information technology.[14]

---

[12] See The American Association for the Advancement of Science, "Congressional Action on Research and Development in the FY 2002 Budget" at <http://www.aaas.org/spp/dspp/rd/ca02main.htm>. The AAAS reports, "There are large increases for basic and applied research in FY2002, especially in NIH. The total federal investment in research is $48.2 billion, an increase of 11.0 percent or $4.8 billion over FY2001. NIH remains the largest single sponsor of basic and applied research; in FY2002, NIH alone will fund 46 percent of all federal support of research. All federal agencies receive increases for their research portfolios, especially agencies with defense or counter-terrorism programs." (p.3)

[13] See National Research Council, *Capitalizing on New Needs and New Opportunities, Government-Industry Partnerships in Biotechnology and Information Technologies, op.cit.*, p. 30 and 63.

[14] As the Committee's study on new needs and opportunities in biotechnology and information technologies finds, multidisciplinary approaches are increasingly required in science and engineering research. Specifically, the Committee has found that "biotechnology and information technology R&D each provide tools and models useful to the other. Interdependencies also exist among chemistry, physics, and structural biology, and among mathematics, computer engineering, and genomics. Further examples of these interdependencies can be found in the complementary roles in the physical

e. Investments in a broad portfolio of disciplines with special emphasis on programs to bridge the gap among disciplines are important to the long-term health of the U.S. innovation system.
f. In many instances efforts underway in the United States to support disciplines sustaining the technologies of the future do not match the rapid growth seen in corresponding foreign efforts. Over time this may negatively affect the relative competitiveness of U.S. firms in the global marketplace and may slow the overall pace of innovation in the United States.

VI. The case of the semiconductor industry illustrates that partnerships have contributed directly to furthering the global competitiveness of U.S. industry.

a. Leading industrialists from the United States and abroad believe that the U.S. experiment with a government-industry partnership, i.e., the SEMATECH consortium, contributed to the resurgence of the U.S. semiconductor industry.[15]
b. One consequence of this perception of SEMATECH is that many countries around the world are engaged in substantial cooperative efforts to support technological advances in their national or regional semiconductor industry.[16] The relative scope of these cooperative efforts and

---

sciences and engineering in nano-scale semiconductor work, and in the overall important role engineering plays in providing new research tools and diagnostics in all of these areas." See National Research Council, *Capitalizing on New Needs and New Opportunities, Government-Industry Partnerships in Biotechnology and Information Technologies, op cit.*, part III, p. 65.

[15]Leading Japanese industrialists have noted the contributions of U.S. partnerships in semiconductors. As Hajime Susaki, Chairman of NEC Corporation noted, "A major factor contributing to the U.S. semiconductor industry's recovery from this perilous situation [in the 1980s] was a U.S. national policy based around cooperation between industry, government, and academia." ("Japanese Semiconductor Industry's Competitiveness: LSI Industry in Jeopardy," Nikkei Microdevices, December 2000) Further, Hitachi's Toshiaki Masuhara observes in his review of government-university-university collaboration in the United States that there has been a good balance of support by government and industry for research through the universities. This has included "a very good balance between design and processing." He adds that the overall success of U.S. industry appears to have come from the contributions of five overlapping efforts. These include the SIA roadmap to determine the direction of research; the planning of resource allocation by SIA and SRC; the allocation of federal funding through the Department of Defense, National Science Foundation, and the Defense Advanced Research Projects Agency; the success of SEMATECH and International SEMATECH in supporting research on process, technology, design, and testing; and The Focus Center Research Project. See Dr. Masuhara's comments in the proceedings of National Research Council, *Securing the Future: Regional and National Programs to Support the Semiconductor Industry, op.cit.* See also Kenneth Flamm and Qifei Wang, "SEMATECH Revisited: Assessing Consortium Impacts on Semiconductor Industry R&D" in National Research Council, *Securing the Future, op. cit.*

[16]See Thomas R. Howell, "Competing Programs: Government Support for Microelectronics," in National Research Council, *Securing the Future: Regional and National Programs to Support the Semiconductor Industry, op. cit.*

the level of funding for these programs are substantially greater in other producer countries than in the United States.[17] Over time, these R&D efforts are likely to bear fruit and may alter the technological and competitive position of the U.S. industry.

VII. Properly constructed, operated, and evaluated partnerships can provide an effective means for accelerating the progress of technology from the laboratory to the market.

a. Public-private partnerships have become an integral and growing part of the U.S. innovation system. The public-private cooperation they engender is—and will remain—an effective means for the creation, transfer, and dissemination of new welfare-enhancing technologies.

b. Doctrinal views on the appropriateness of government-industry cooperation overlook the reality of its contribution to the development of the United States in the past, understate the contributions of such cooperation in the present, and run the risk of compromising positive contributions in the future.

c. The Committee's endorsement of the role of partnerships in the U.S. innovation system must, however, be put in context. Uncritical enthusiasm for partnerships as panaceas is certainly misplaced. On the other hand, blanket disparagement of partnerships as "corporate welfare" is equally misplaced, not least because it overlooks the pragmatic approaches to technology development throughout U.S. history and the need to continue constructive experiments today.

[17]See National Research Council, *Securing the Future: Regional and National Programs to Support the Semiconductor Industry, op. cit.*

RECOMMENDATIONS

I. Regular and rigorous program-based evaluations and feedback is essential for effective partnerships and should be a standard feature. Greater policy attention and resources to the systematic evaluation of U.S. and foreign partnerships should be encouraged.

a. Evaluation must include real metrics reflecting the specific goals of the partnership, with the additional recognition that rapidly evolving technologies may well require goals and metrics that evolve over time. New national needs (e.g., combating terrorism) may also necessitate new objectives. Existing partnership programs such as ATP and SBIR bring core competencies well suited to these needs.

b. Evaluations should occur with some frequency and regularity and should include analysis of both project successes and failures. The failure of a particular project need not imply the failure of a program as a whole. The willingness to cancel under-performing projects is essential.

c. For evaluations to be effective their findings must be integrated into program operations. Learning from previous and current experience can improve the performance of partnerships and enable them to adapt to better capitalize on emerging needs and new opportunities.[18]

II. Learning from competitive and comparative experiences in the global economy is also vital for effective U.S. policy on partnerships and foreign policies and programs should be regularly assessed.

a. In a global economy, what the rest of the world thinks and does is important; both because we may learn from policy experiments in other countries and because the measures they take may affect the competitive position of U.S. firms and industries. The U.S. approach to innovation is not the only model for success.

b. The competitive and emulative element in programs abroad should not mask the opportunities and needs for mutually beneficial cooperation. Such cooperation is particularly relevant in the global semiconductor industry as it faces unprecedented technical challenges associated with sustaining Moore's Law.[19]

---

[18]The ATP program at NIST and the Fast Track program initiated at the Department of Defense are examples of regular evaluation and the integration of its lessons in program operations. See National Research Council, *The Advanced Technology Program—Assessing Outcomes*, *op.cit.*, and National Research Council, *SBIR—An Assessment of the Department of Defense Fast Track Initiative*, *op.cit.*

[19]See Gordon E. Moore, "Cramming more components onto integrated circuits," *Electronics* 38(8) April 19, 1965. Here, Dr. Moore notes that "[t]he complexity for minimum component costs has increased at a rate of roughly a factor of two per year. Certainly over the short term, this rate can be expected to continue, if not to increase. Over the longer term, the rate of increase is a bit more uncertain, although there is no reason to believe it will not remain nearly constant for at least 10 years.

III. Partnerships should be embarked on a case-by-case basis and should draw, where applicable, on previous experience.

a. The Committee's analysis strongly suggests that partnerships do make positive contributions in the right circumstances. Determining what those circumstances are and what type of partnership would be most appropriate represents a constructive challenge for policy makers. There is no "one size fits all" solution. Additional research—through intermittent comparisons and evaluations—could advance our understanding of the conditions for successful public-private partnerships.

b. Partnerships that are appropriately constructed and carefully and regularly evaluated offer society a proven means of enhancing both the welfare of our citizens and the security of the nation.

c. National policy with regard to partnerships should be flexible, fostering a culture of experimentation. It should include, as appropriate, features such as industry initiation (i.e., a bottom-up, not a top-down approach), industry leadership, defined limits to public commitments of resources, clear objectives, cost sharing, and learning through ongoing evaluation of the experiences of previous and current partnerships both in the United States and abroad.

IV. Strengthening public support for research in physics, chemistry, mechanical and electrical engineering, and materials science and engineering should be a national priority. These disciplines underpin continued advances in information technology, a source of economic growth, and are essential for continued progress in the area of health care through information technology-based advances in biomedicine.

a. Significant increases in funding for physical sciences and engineering—including material sciences, chemistry, physics, and electrical engineering—are needed to build greater understanding of properties of nanostructures underpinning tomorrow's information industries as well to capitalize on advances in biotechnology.[20]

b. Renewed policy attention is required to encourage cooperative research in information technologies, the disciplines that support them, and in

---

That means by 1975, the number of components per integrated circuit for minimum cost will be 65,000." See also, Gordon E. Moore, "The Continuing Silicon Technology Evolution Inside the PC Platform," *Intel Developer Update,* Issue 2, October 15, 1997, where he notes that he "first observed the 'doubling of transistor density on a manufactured die every year' in 1965, just four years after the first planar integrated circuit was discovered. The press called this 'Moore's Law' and the name has stuck. To be honest, I did not expect this law to still be true some 30 years later, but I am now confident that it will be true for another 20 years."

[20]See the recommendations and findings in National Research Council, *Capitalizing on New Needs and New Opportunities, Government-Industry Partnerships in Biotechnology and Information Technologies, op.cit.*

other promising sectors such as biotechnology. In particular, the level and distribution of resources and the evolving roles of universities, laboratories, and private investors require innovative policy responses. By bringing together various actors, public-private partnerships can make a valuable contribution to the long-term welfare and security of the United States and its continued leadership in the global economy.[21]

[21] *Ibid.*

III

AN ENVIRONMENT FOR INNOVATION

An Environment for Innovation

THE POLICY CONTEXT OF GROWTH

The U.S. system of government and the policies developed at federal, state, and local levels collectively shape the environment in which innovation takes place. For example, federal policies affecting capital formation and corporate governance play important roles in competitive performance.[1] The range and diversity of these policies are substantial. They include government policies related to taxation, especially capital gains, fiscal and monetary matters, education and training, trade promotion and expansion, regulatory policies (e.g., for antitrust and the environment), intellectual property protection, government procurement, and export control.[2] These policies can all directly affect the process of innovation, sometimes decisively.[3]

---

[1]See National Research Council, *U.S. Industry in 2000: Studies in Competitive Performance, op.cit,* p. 5.

[2]See, for example, the observations of Ed Zchau, a member of Congress in the 1980s from Silicon Valley, in his article, "Government Policies for Innovation and Growth" in National Research Council, *The Positive Sum Strategy, Harnessing Technology for Economic Growth, op.cit.*, pp. 535-539.

[3]For example, intellectual property protection plays a key role in the continued development of the biotechnology industry. See Wesley M. Cohen and John Walsh, "Public Research, Patents and Implications for Industrial R&D in the Drug, Biotechnology, Semiconductor and Computer Industries" in National Research Council, *Capitalizing on New Needs and New Opportunities: Government-Industry Partnerships in Biotechnology and Information Technologies, op. cit.* Trade policy also has a major, if often unrecognized, impact on innovation. Restrictive trade policy can slow innovation (e.g., by restricting the acquisition of low-cost information technology systems and components) as in Brazil in the 1990s. See National Research Council, *U.S. Industry in 2000, Studies in Competitive Performance, op. cit.*, pp. 4-5. It can also encourage the growth of national industries. The resurgence

The pace of technology development also depends on a variety of interrelated factors, beginning with the performance of educational organizations and the quality of scientific and engineering research carried out by public and private institutions. The strength and depth of U.S. capital markets also play a major role in availability and cost of capital.[4] Public policies designed to develop, commercialize, and absorb new technologies further strengthen prospects for improved welfare and rapid economic growth.[5]

The core mission of the Committee on Government-Industry Partnerships is examining how public policy can stimulate the wide range of benefits technological advance can provide—from more robust economic growth to better health, from more environmentally benign energy use to more effective and lower-cost national defense. The committee's focus on the policies that support and facilitate the development and exchange of knowledge—as within and among private firms, universities, and national laboratories—is therefore both practical and necessary. This is especially true given the increasing emphasis on the link between science and economic growth.

Box A. New Growth Theory and the Knowledge-Based Economy

Neoclassical theories of growth long emphasized the role of labor and capital as inputs.[6] Here, technology was *exogenous*—assumed to be determined by forces external to the economic system. More recent growth theories, by comparison, emphasize the role of technology and assume that technology is *endogenous*—that is, it is actually integral to the performance of the economic system. Contributions to this academic literature come from industrial organization as well as evolutionary and

of the U.S. semiconductor industry, now taken for granted, was not assured in the mid-1980s. The industry's resurgence arose partly through the contribution of measures to open Japanese markets and reduce dumping in the United States and third countries partly through the contributions of SEMATECH and, most importantly, the ability of U.S. firms to develop new product lines and to continue to attract capital contributed to the recovery and prosperity of the U.S. semiconductor industry. No one factor fully accounts for this recovery.

[4]See Ralph Landau, "The Dynamics of Long-Term Growth: Gaining and Losing Advantage in the Chemical Industry" in National Research Council, *U.S. Industry in 2000, op. cit.*, p. 20.

[5]See Ralph Landau, *op. cit.*, pp. 17-74.

[6]See Robert S. Solow, "Technical Change and the Aggregate Production Function," *Review of Economics and Statistics* 39, 1957, pp. 312–320 for a classic expression of the "old" growth theory.

institutional economics.[7] Prominent among these endogenous explanations is the New Growth Theory, which has integrated and formalized many of these insights and observations into a coherent economic theory.[8]

Growth theory advocates underscore the importance of investing in new knowledge creation to sustain growth. It requires in turn that policy makers pay careful attention to the multiple factors that contribute to knowledge creation, including research and development, the education system, entrepreneurship, and an openness to trade and investment.

Geography of economic development

The new economic growth theory emphasizes the role of technology creation, believed to be characterized by significant growth externalities.[9] A consequence of the renewed appreciation of growth externalities is the growing focus on the economic geography of economic development. With growth externalities coming about in part from the exchanges of knowledge among innovators, certain regions become centers for particular types of high-growth activities. Innovators are able to take advantage of the tacit knowledge available in such centers or clusters of activity to acquire relevant technological innovation and to address other business development issues rapidly.[10]

---

[7]The broader literature includes Alfred Marshall, *Industry and Trade,* 3rd edition, Macmillan, London, 1920. Nathan Rosenberg, *Inside the Black Box: Technology and Economics,* New York: Cambridge University Press, 1982; Douglass C. North, *Institutions, Institutional Change, and Economic Performance,* Cambridge, MA: Cambridge University Press, 1990; Richard R. Nelson, *The Sources of Economic Growth,* Cambridge, MA: Harvard University Press, 2000; and F.M. Scherer, *New Perspectives on Economic Growth and Technological Innovation,* Washington, D.C.: The Brookings Institution, 1999.

[8]For additional perspective on New Growth Theory, see Richard N. Langlois, "Knowledge, consumption, and endogenous growth," *Journal of Evolutionary Economics* 11: 77-93, 2001.

[9]Paul Romer, "Endogenous technological change," *Journal of Political Economy,* vol. 98, 1990, p. 71-102. See also Gene Grossman and Elhanan Helpman, *Innovation and Growth in the Global Economy,* Cambridge, MA: MIT Press, 1993.

[10]See Michael Porter, "Clusters and the New Economics of Competition," *Harvard Business Review,* November – December 1998. Also, Paul Krugman, *Geography and Trade,* Cambridge, MA: MIT Press, 1991, p. 23, who points out Alfred Marshall's observation in his classic *Principles of Economics* that geographic clusters of specific economic activities arise from the exchange of "tacit" knowledge among business people. AnnaLee Saxenian's review of the growth of Silicon Valley provides one view of the cluster phenomenon. AnnaLee Saxenian, *Regional Advantage: Culture and Competition in Silicon Valley and Route 128,* Cambridge, MA: Harvard University Press, 1994. For a perspective on the federal role in Silicon Valley, see Timothy Sturgeon, "How Silicon Valley Came to Be," in Martin Kenney, ed., *Understanding Silicon Valley, The Anatomy of an Entrepreneurial Region,* Stanford: Stanford University Press, 2000.

Locational competition and trade policy

The growing understanding of the importance of knowledge and the clusters that generate and retain it has led policy makers outside the United States to adopt trade, investment, and competition policies that while appearing to derive from U.S. precepts, are in fact much more focused on positive outcomes of the national economy, rather than on rules and processes. Even in the United States improved understanding of the institutional context of economic growth has led some economists to suggest limitations to traditional trade theory, particularly with respect to the reality of imperfect international competition.[11] Further, economic analysis suggests that high technology is often characterized by increasing rather than decreasing returns, justifying to some the proposition that governments can capture permanent advantage in key industries by providing relatively small but potentially decisive support to assist national industries up the learning curve and down the cost curve. In part, this is why the economic literature now recognizes the relationship between technology policy and trade policy.[12] Recognition of these linkages and the corresponding ability of governments to shift comparative advantage in favor of the national economy provide the intellectual underpinning for government support for high-technology industry.[13]

Spillovers

Another widely recognized rationale for government support of high technology exists when technology generates benefits beyond those that can be captured by innovating firms, often referred to as spillovers.[14] As a related and important example, consider the case in which the cost of a given technology may be prohibitive for individual companies even though expected benefits to society are substantial and widespread.[15]

---

[11]See Paul Krugman, *Rethinking International Trade,* Cambridge, MA: MIT Press, 1990.

[12]See J.A. Brander and B.J. Spencer, "International R&D Rivalry and Industrial Strategy," *Review of Economic Studies,* vol. 50, 1983, pp. 707-722, and "Export Subsidies and International Market Share Rivalry, " *Journal of International Economics,* vol. 16, 1985, pp. 83-100.

[13]For a discussion of governments' efforts to capture new technologies and the industries they spawn for their national economies, see National Research Council, *Conflict and Cooperation in National Competition for High Technology Industry,* op.cit., pp. 28-40. For a critique of these efforts, see P. Krugman, *Peddling Prosperity: Economic Sense and Nonsense in an Age of Diminished Expectations.* New York: W.W. Norton Press, 1994.

[14]See, for example, Martin N. Baily and A. Chakrabati, *Innovation and the Productivity Crisis.* Washington, D.C.: Brookings, 1998, and Zvi Griliches, *The Search for R&D Spillovers,* Cambridge, MA: Harvard University Press, 1990.

[15]See Ishaq Nadiri, *Innovations and Technological Spillovers,* NBER Working Paper No. 4423, 1993, and Edwin Mansfield, "Academic Research and Industrial Innovation," *Research Policy,* February, 1991. See also Council of Economic Advisers, *Supporting Research and Development to Promote Economic Growth: The Federal Government's Role.* Washington, D.C., 1995. This is one of the rationales for the awards of the Advanced Technology Program. For an assessment of this program, see National Research Council, *The Advanced Technology Program: Assessing Outcomes, op.cit.*

The increasing recognition of the dynamic element of technological innovation, in particular its cumulative nature, has provided the intellectual underpinning as well as the incentive to spur local, state, and national efforts to create competitive advantage for a region, country, or industry.[16]

Knowledge-based economics

To a considerable extent, knowledge-based economies are distinguished by the changing way that firms do business and how governments respond in terms of policy.[17] Key features of a knowledge-based economy include:

- A capacity to successfully create and exploit scientific knowledge and technology based on a world-class science infrastructure and an entrepreneurial and innovative culture.
- A diffusion and building up of knowledge through effective (though often informal) information networks. These networks, facilitated by modern telecommunication technologies and frequently based on public-private partnerships, are designed to encourage cooperation among firms, universities, and government research centers.
- A skilled workforce based on an effective and differentiated educational system and effective job training programs.
- High rates of technological innovation often associated with high-technology industries, underscoring the "virtuous cycle" that these policies can engender.

THE PACE OF TECHNOLOGY DEVELOPMENT AND GROWTH

U.S. policy makers at the state and federal levels have focused their attention increasingly on high-technology industry and the new technologies and entrepreneurial activities that support them.[18] Their concern is supported by a growing

[16]The dynamic nature of international competition in high-technology industries is discussed in National Research Council, *Conflict and Cooperation in National Competition for High-Technology Industry,* 1996, *op. cit.,* pp. 28-40.

[17]"Just as the private sector develops innovative institutional arrangements to support and advance research, so should federal policy. In particular, one of the defining features of the knowledge economy is the increased importance of learning and innovation. Partnerships and alliances, among the private sector, universities, and government laboratories, play a key role in facilitating innovation. As a result, federal support for research in the knowledge economy needs to explicitly encourage research collaboration between industry, government labs and universities." Kenan Patrick Jarboe and Robert D. Atkinson, "The Case for Technology in the Knowledge Economy; R&D, Economic Growth and the Role of Government," Washington, D.C.: Progressive Policy Institute, June 1, 1998, at <http://www.ppionline.org/documents/CaseforTech.pdf>.

[18]See for example, previous and current reports of the Council of Economic Advisors, *Economic Report of the President*, Washington, D.C.: USGPO, January 1995, 2001, and 2002.

body of economic thought, noted above in Box A, that the composition of the economy matters and that high technology industries in particular bring special benefits to national economies.[19] This political interest, particularly at the state level in the United States, reflects the intense interest of national and regional leaders elsewhere in the world in the composition and growth of their economies.

As previous National Research Council studies have described, high-technology firms are associated with rapid rates of innovation. Such firms in turn tend to gain market share, create new product markets, and use resources more productively than traditional industries do.[20] High-technology firms perform more R&D than traditional firms do and generate more high-wage employment. In fact, these firms are distinguished by the high percentage of revenue devoted to research: 10 percent of revenues on R&D, in contrast to 3 percent of revenues on R&D for more traditional industries.[21]

Reflecting this investment, high-technology firms also create positive spillover effects, which are often locally concentrated. Spillovers benefit other commercial sectors by generating new products and processes that can lead to productivity gains. A substantial literature in economics underscores the potential for high returns from technological innovation, with private innovators obtaining rates of return in the 20-30 percent range and spillover (or social return) averaging about 50 percent.[22]

High-technology products are a major source of growth in the major industrialized countries. Such sectors as aerospace, biotechnology, and information systems contribute to the growing global market for high-technology manufactured goods. High-technology firms are also associated with high value-added manufacturing and with the creation of high-wage employment.[23] Together these contributions provide the productivity gains that underpin recent economic performance. (See Box B for detail.) They also enhance the government's capacity to

[19]See for example, Stephen Oliner and Daniel Sichel, "The Resurgence of Growth in the late 1990's: Is Information Technology the Story?" *Journal of Economic Perspectives* 14(4) Fall 2000. Oliner and Sichel estimate that improvements in the computer industry's own productive processes account for about a quarter of the overall productivity increase. They also note that the use of information technology by all sorts of companies accounts for nearly half the rise in productivity. See also Laura Tyson, *Who's Bashing Whom? Trade Conflict in High Tech Industries,* Washington, D.C.: Institute for International Economics, 1992. Tyson notes that substantial advantages in trade accrue to nations that directly support strategic industries.

[20]For an analysis of the role of new information technologies in the recent trends in high productivity growth, often described as the New Economy, see the Council of Economic Advisors, *Economic Report of the President,* H. Doc. 107-2, Washington, D.C.: USGPO, January 2001.

[21]See National Research Council, *Conflict and Cooperation,* 1996, *op. cit.* Box A, pp. 33-35, lists additional reasons why countries are concerned about their high-technology industries.

[22]For example, see Ishaq Nadiri, *op. cit.* See also, Council of Economic Advisors, *Supporting Research and Development to Promote Economic Growth, op. cit.*

[23]Laura Tyson, *Who's Bashing Whom? Trade Conflict in High Technology Industries, op. cit.*

carry out core missions, including national defense, environmental protection, and development of new technologies for the production, management, and use of energy.[24]

The advantages of high technology industry are not without a downside. As is evident in the current economic climate, the high technology sector tends also to be characterized by considerable cyclicality. Pronounced swings in industry products and profits can precipitate layoffs and rapid depreciation in the value of stock, thus affecting the lives of ordinary citizens in very direct ways. At the same time, the industry's long-term growth trend has been exceptionally positive, contributing significantly to employment and value creation.

Government support for new technologies contributes to continual national growth and industrial leadership. Policies encouraging partnerships and other cooperative arrangements among universities, industry, and the government have proven in some cases to be effective measures for fostering the development of new productivity-enhancing technologies.[25] Often such policies are related to specific government missions and procurement in sectors such as health, transport, and defense.[26] In other cases, limited support to promising technologies with widespread applications may be the most appropriate approach.[27] Indeed, as we see next, there is a long tradition of federal support to industry, dating from the founding of the republic.

Box B. The New Economy

The term "New Economy" has been used extensively in recent years to describe the economic performance of the latter part of the 1990s. The term focuses on the dynamic of the U.S. economy as it capitalizes on new technologies, new opportunities, and in particular on national investments in computing, information, and communication technologies—or collectively, information technology. As we note below, use of the term New Economy also reflects the growing conviction that sub-

[24]For environmental gains achieved through reduced energy demand resulting from improved energy efficiency, see, the presentation of Charles Becker in National Research Council, *Partnerships for Solid-State Lighting*, C. Wessner, ed., Washington, D.C.: National Academy Press, 2002.

[25]See Kenneth Flamm, *Creating the Computer, Government,* Industry and High Technology, Washington, D.C.: Brookings, 1988.

[26]See National Research Council, *The Small Business Innovation Research Program: An Assessment of the Department of Defense Fast Track Initiative.* C. Wessner, ed., Washington, D.C.: National Academy Press, 2000.

[27]This is the approach taken by the ATP at the National Institute of Standards and Technology. For an overview of government-industry collaboration and the controversies that surround it, see the introduction to the recent report on the ATP, National Research Council, *The Advanced Technology Program: Assessing Outcomes, op. cit.*

stantial change has occurred in the structure of the U.S. economy and that this change may be permanent.[28] This change, it is thought, hinges on dynamic increases in productivity and the correlating impact of investments in the information technology sector.[29]

These structural changes indicate that the New Economy is not a fad, but a long-term productivity shift of major significance. The introduction of advanced productivity-enhancing technologies obviously does not eliminate the business cycle. Instead, the term, "New Economy" refers to particular technological and structural changes that are having a positive impact on long-term productivity and growth.[30]

The decade of the 1990s witnessed rapid technological change in communications, computing, and information management. This phenomenon coincided with the sustained expansion of the U.S. economy through much of the 1990s.[31] Along with other structural and policy explanations, this technological change is a key element in the strong growth in labor productivity, especially after 1995.[32] The term New Economy captures the role that these new technologies are thought to play in contributing to the non-inflationary growth and high employment that characterized this period.

Although the New Economy is itself a macro phenomenon, its underlying dynamics appear to combine elements of technological innovation, structural change, and public policy.

- *Technological innovation*—more accurately, the rapid rate of technological innovation in information technology (including computers, software, and telecommunications) and the rapid growth of the Internet—

[28]Organisation for Economic Cooperation and Development, *Is There a New Economy? A First Report on the OECD Growth Project.* Paris: Organisation for Economic Cooperation and Development, June 2000, p. 17. See also, M.N. Baily and R.Z. Lawrence. "Do We Have an E-Conomy?" NBER Working Paper 8243, April 23, 2001, at <http://www.nber.org/papers/w8243>.

[29]This is especially so for the computer hardware sector and perhaps for the Internet as well, although there is insufficient empirical evidence on the degree to which the Internet may be responsible. For a discussion of the impact of the Internet on economic growth see, "A Thinker's Guide," *The Economist,* March 30, 2000. For a broad study of investment in technology capital and its use in various sectors, see McKinsey Global Institute, *U.S. Productivity Growth 1995-2000, Understanding the Contribution of Information Technology Relative to Other Factors.* Washington, D.C.: McKinsey & Co., October 2001.

[30]See Council of Economic Advisors, *The Annual Report of the Council of Economic Advisors,* Washington, D.C.: U.S. Government Printing Office, 2000, p. 33.

[31]See Dale Jorgenson and Kevin Stiroh, "Raising the Speed Limit: U.S. Economic Growth in the Information Age," *Brookings Papers-on-Economic-Activity*; 0(1), 2000, pp. 125-211.

[32]*Ibid.*

are seen by some as underpinning the productivity gains that characterize the New Economy. These productivity gains derive from greater efficiencies in the production of computers and from expanded use of information technologies.[33]

- *Structural changes* arise from a reconfiguration of knowledge networks and business patterns made possible by innovations in information technology. Such phenomena as business-to-business e-commerce and Internet retailing are altering how firms and individuals interact, enabling greater efficiency in purchases, production processes, and inventory management.[34] These structural changes are still emerging as the use and applications of the Internet continue to evolve.[35]
- *Public policy* plays a major role at several levels. This includes the government's role in fostering rules of interaction within the Internet and its discretion in setting and enforcing the rules by which technology firms and others compete.[36] More familiarly, public policy concerns particular fiscal and regulatory choices that can affect the rate and focus of investments in sectors such as telecommunications. The government also plays a critical role in the innovation system.[37] It provides national research capacities, incentives to promote education and training in critical disciplines, and funds most of the nation's basic research.[38] The government also plays a major role in stimulating innovation, most broadly through the patent system. Through its policies on taxation, bankruptcy, and capital market regulation, the government has encouraged entrepreneurs who, as agents of change,

[33]See Stephen Oliner and Daniel Sichel, "The Resurgence of Growth in the late 1990's: Is Information Technology the Story?" *op. cit.* See also Alan Greenspan's remarks before the White House Conference on the New Economy, Washington, D.C., April 5, 2000. <www.federalreserve.gov/BOARDDOCS/SPEECHES/2000/20000405.HTM>.

[34]See, for example, Brookes Martin and Zaki Wahhaj, "The Shocking Economic Impact of B2B" *Global Economic Paper,* 37, Goldman Sachs, February 3, 2000.

[35]For a discussion of the opportunities and challenges facing the New Economy, see National Research Council, *Measuring and Sustaining the New Economy.* D. Jorgenson and C. Wessner, eds., Washington, D.C.: National Academy Press, 2002. In particular, see comments by Dr. Vint Cerf, who notes that the ability of individuals to interact in potentially useful ways within the infrastructure of the still expanding Internet rests on its basic rule architecture: "The reason it can function is that all the networks use the same set of protocols. An important point is these networks are run by different administrations, which must collaborate both technically and economically on a global scale."

[36]The relevance of competition policy to the New Economy is manifested by the intensity of interest in the antitrust case, *United States versus Microsoft,* and associated policy issues.

[37]See Richard Nelson, ed., *National Innovation Systems,* New York: Oxford University Press, 1993.

[38]See National Research Council, *Trends in Federal Support of Research in Graduate Education,* Washington, D.C.: National Academy Press, 2001.

bring new ideas and new technologies to the marketplace.[39] Government procurement and awards are especially powerful in the development of new technologies to fulfill national missions in defense, health, and the environment.[40] Collectively, these public policies have played and continue to play a central role in the development of the modern economy. The collective contributions of these technologies, especially information technology, are contributing to structural change in the U.S. economy.

Adapted from National Research Council, *Measuring and Sustaining the New Economy,* D. Jorgenson and C. Wessner, eds., Washington, D.C.: National Academy Press, 2002.

[39]In addition to government-funded research, intellectual property protection plays an essential role in the continued development of the biotechnology industry. See Wesley M. Cohen and John Walsh, "Public Research, Patents and Implications for Industrial R&D in the Drug, Biotechnology, Semiconductor and Computer Industries" in National Research Council, *Capitalizing on New Needs and New Opportunities: Government-Industry Partnerships in Biotechnology and Information Technologies, op. cit.*

[40]For example, government support played a critical role in the early development of computers. See Kenneth Flamm, *Creating the Computer,* Washington, D.C.: Brookings, 1988. The Committee's study of public-private partnerships has not systematically explored the important role of government procurement.

IV

FEDERAL PARTNERSHIPS WITH INDUSTRY: PAST, PRESENT, AND FUTURE

Federal Partnerships with Industry: Past, Present, and Future

A BRIEF HISTORY OF FEDERAL SUPPORT[1]

The earliest articulation of the government's nurturing role with regard to the composition of the economy was Alexander Hamilton's 1791 *Report on Manufacture,* in which he urged an activist approach by the federal government. At that time, Hamilton's emphasis on industrial development was controversial, although subsequent U.S. policy has largely reflected his belief in the need for an active federal role in the development of the U.S. economy.[2] In fact, driven by the exigencies of national defense and the requirements of transportation and communication across the North American Continent, the federal government in that same decade played an instrumental role in developing new production techniques and technologies by turning to individual entrepreneurs with innovative ideas. Most notably the federal government in 1798 aided the foundation of the first

[1]See Vernon W. Ruttan, *Technology, Growth and Development: An Induced Innovation Perspective.* New York: Cambridge University Press, 2001, page 588. See also Audretsch *et al.*, "The Economics of Science and Technology," *op cit.* pp. 158-164, for additional historical background of U.S. policy in the area of science and technology.

[2]The rejection of Hamilton's report, though often portrayed as a reluctance on the part of the new federal government to promote development, reflected the decision of the political leadership of the time to place priority on agricultural rather than industrial development. The exception to this was in the area of military procurement, with the contract to Eli Whitney's Springfield Arsenal. See William Diebold, Jr., "Past and Future Industrial Policy in the United States," in J. Pinder, ed., *National Industrial Strategies and the World Economy*, London: Allanheld, Osmun & Co., 1980.

machine tool industry with a contract to the inventor Eli Whitney for interchangeable musket parts.[3]

A few decades later, in 1842, Congress appropriated funds to demonstrate the feasibility of Samuel Morse's telegraph.[4] Both Whitney and Morse fostered significant innovations that led to completely new industries. Indeed, Morse's innovation was the first step on the road to today's networked planet. The support for Morse was not an isolated case. The federal government increasingly saw economic development as central to its responsibilities. During the nineteenth century, the federal government played an instrumental role in developing the U.S. railway network through the Pacific Railroad Act of 1862 and the Union Pacific Act of 1864.[5] While not without abuse, these acts provided very substantial financial incentives to the development of the U.S. rail network. The federal

---

[3]The 1798 contract with Eli Whitney was an early example of high-technology procurement. Whitney missed his first delivery date for the arms and encountered substantial cost overruns, a set of events that is still familiar. However, his focus on the concept of interchangeable parts and the machine tools to make them was prescient. David A. Hounshell, in his excellent analysis of the development of manufacturing technology in the United States, suggests that Simeon North was in fact the one who succeeded in achieving interchangeability and the production of components by special-purpose machinery. See *From the American System to Mass Production, 1800-1932*, Baltimore: Johns Hopkins University Press, 1985, pp. 25-32. By the 1850s the United States had begun to export specialized machine tools to the Enfield Arsenal in Great Britain. The British described the large-scale production of firearms, made with interchangeable parts, as "the American system of manufacturers." See David C. Mowery and Nathan Rosenberg, *Paths of Innovation: Technological Change in 20th Century America*, New York: Cambridge University Press, 1998, p. 6. Whitney's concept of interchangeable parts and the machine tools to make them was in the end successful.

[4]For a discussion of Samuel Morse's 1837 application for a grant and the congressional debate, see Irwin Lebow, *Information Highways and Byways*. New York: Institute of Electrical and Electronics Engineers, 1995, pp. 9-12. For a more detailed account, see Robert Luther Thompson, *Wiring a Continent: The History of the Telegraph Industry in the United States 1823-1836*. Princeton, N.J.: Princeton University Press, 1947.

[5]For an economic history of the transcontinental railroad, see Robert W. Fogel, *Railroads and American Economic Growth: Essays in Econometric History,* Baltimore: Johns Hopkins University Press, 1964. See also Alfred P. Chandler, *Strategy and Structure: Chapters in History of the Industrial Enterprise*, Cambridge, MA: MIT Press, 1962. For a popular historical account, see Stephen Ambrose, *Nothing Like It in the World: The Men Who Built the Transcontinental Railroad 1863-1869,* New York: Simon and Schuster, 2000. In the midst of the Civil War, Abraham Lincoln signed the Pacific Railroad Act of 1862 providing the necessary standards and substantial incentives to launch the first transcontinental railroad. Financial aid to the railroads was provided in the form of government bonds at $16,000 to $48,000 per mile depending on terrain, as well as land grants for stations, machine shops, etc. In addition, right of way was to extend 200 feet on both sides of the road. The Pacific Railroad Act was supplemented in 1864 by the Union Pacific Act, which did not increase government funding but allowed the railroad companies to issue their own first-mortgage bonds. This act also allowed President Lincoln to set the "standard gauge" at 4 feet, 8 1/2 inches. As with fiber-optic investments today, there was some overbuilding, but the fundamental policy objectives of national unity and economic growth were achieved. From 30,000 miles of railway in 1860, rail mileage grew to more than 201,000 by 1900, linking the nation together.

government also played a key role in developing the farm sector through the 1862 Morrill Act,[6] which established state agricultural and engineering colleges; the 1889 Hatch Act, which established state agricultural experiment stations; and the 1914 Smith Lever Act, which added state agricultural extension services.[7] The Union Pacific act made it possible to build one of the world's great transportation systems. It was also for its time a major partnership, both because market incentives were not sufficient and because the government provided major financial inducement to encourage this massive undertaking. The inducements were on the scale of the enterprise—and not without abuse—but the fundamental policy objectives of economic growth and national unity were achieved.

There were also major benefits in terms of management, organization, and market scale for many other American firms—what economists today would call positive externalities—created by the extension of a national railroad network. Alfred Chandler has observed that

> As the first private enterprises in the United States with modern administrative structures, the railroads provided industrialists with useful precedents for organization building . . . . More than this, the building of the railroads, more than any other single factor, made possible this growth of the great industrial enterprise. By speedily enlarging the market for American manufacturing, mining, and marketing firms, the railroads permitted and, in fact, often required that these enterprises expand and subdivide their activities.[8]

This support continued and expanded into the twentieth century. In 1901, the federal government established the National Bureau of Standards to coordinate a patchwork of locally and regionally applied standards, which often arbitrary, were a source of confusion in commerce and a hazard to consumers. Later the federal government provided special backing for the development of (what we now call) dual-use industries, such as aircraft frames and engines and radio, seen as important to the nation's security and commerce. The National Advisory Committee for Aeronautics, formed in 1915, contributed to the development of the U.S. aircraft industry, a role the government still plays.[9] Similarly, the Navy was instru-

---

[6]The Morrill Act of 1862 established the land grant college system. It charged each state with establishing at least one college in the agricultural and mechanical sciences. Each state was given 30,000 acres of federal land per member of Congress.

[7]See Robert E. Evanson and Wallace E. Huffman, Science for Agriculture: A Long-term Perspective, Ames: Iowa State University Press, 1993. See Richard Bingham, *Industrial Policy American Style: From Hamilton to HDTV*, New York: M.E. Sharpe, 1998 for a broader review.

[8]Alfred D. Chandler, *Strategy and Structure*, *op cit*, p. 21.

[9]See D. Mowery and N. Rosenberg, *Technology and the Pursuit of Economic Growth,* New York: Cambridge University Press, 1989, Chapter 7, especially pp. 181-194. The authors note that the commercial aircraft industry is unique among manufacturing industries in that a federal research organization, the National Advisory Committee on Aeronautics (NACA, founded in 1915 and absorbed by

mental in launching the U.S. radio industry by encouraging patent pooling and by direct participation in the Radio Corporation of America (RCA).[10]

The unprecedented challenges of World War II generated huge increases in the level of government procurement and support for high-technology industries.[11] Today's computing industry has its origins in the government's wartime support for a program that resulted in the creation of the ENIAC, one of the earliest electronic digital computers, and the government's steady encouragement of that fledgling industry in the postwar period.[12] Following World War II the federal government began to fund basic research at universities on a significant scale. This was done first through the Office of Naval Research and later through the National Science Foundation.[13]

These activities were complemented by aggressive procurement efforts during the Cold War, when the government continued to emphasize technological superiority as a means of ensuring U.S. security. Government funds and cost-plus

---

NASA in 1958), conducted and funded research on airframe and propulsion technologies. Before World War II NACA operated primarily as a test center for civilian and military users. NACA made a series of remarkable contributions regarding engine nacelle locations and the NACA cowl for radial air-cooled engines. These innovations, together with improvements in engine fillets based on discoveries at Caltech and the development of monocoque construction, had a revolutionary effect on commercial and military aviation. These inventions made the long-range bomber possible, forced the development of high-speed fighter aircraft, and vastly increased the appeal of commercial aviation. See Lebow, *Information Highways and Byways, op. cit.*; and Alexander Flax, National Academy of Engineering, personal communication, September 1999. See also Roger E. Bilstein, *A History of the NACA and NASA, 1915-1990,* Washington, D.C.: National Aeronautics and Space Administration Office of Management Scientific and Technical Information Division, 1989.

[10]Josephus Daniels, Secretary of the Navy during the Wilson Administration, appeared to feel that monopoly was inherent to the wireless industry, and if that were the case, he believed the monopoly should be American. By pooling patents, providing equity, and encouraging General Electric's participation, the Navy helped to create the Radio Corporation of America. See Irwin Lebow, *Information Highways and Byways: From the Telegraph to the 21st Century,* New York: IEEE Press, 1995, pp. 97-98 and Chapter 12. See also Michael Borrus and Jay Stowsky, "Technology Policy and Economic Growth," BRIE Working Paper 97, April 1997.

[11]See David Mowery, "Collaborative R&D: How Effective Is It?" *Issues in Science and Technology,* 15(1): 37, 1998.

[12]See Kenneth Flamm, *Creating the Computer.* Washington, D.C.: Brookings, 1988, Chapters 1-3.

[13]The National Science Foundation (NSF) was initially seen as the agency that would fund basic scientific research at universities after World War II. Disagreements over the degree of Executive Branch control over the NSF delayed passage of its authorizing legislation until 1950, even though the concept for the agency was first put forth in 1945 in Vannevar Bush's report, *Science: The Endless Frontier.* The Office of Naval Research bridged the gap in basic research funding during those years. For an account of the politics of the NSF's creation, see G. Paschal Zachary, *Endless Frontier: Vannevar Bush, Engineer of the American Century,* New York: The Free Press, 1997, p. 231. See also Daniel Lee Kleinman, *Politics on the Endless Frontier: Postwar Research Policy in the United States,* Durham, N.C.: Duke University Press, 1995.

contracts helped to support enabling technologies, such as semiconductors, new materials, radar, jet engines, missiles, and computer hardware and software.[14]

In the post-Cold War period the evolution of the U.S. economy continues to be marked by the interaction of government-funded research and procurement and the activities of innovative entrepreneurs and leading corporations. In the last decade of the twentieth century government support was essential to progress in such areas as microelectronics, robotics, biotechnology, nanotechnologies, and the investigation of the human genome. Patient government support also played a critical role in the development of the Internet (whose forerunners were funded by the Defense Department and the NSF).[15] Together these technologies make up the foundation of the modern economy.

As Vernon W. Ruttan has observed, "Government has played an important role in technology development and transfer in almost every U.S. industry that has become competitive on a global scale."[16] Importantly, the U.S. economy continues to be distinguished by the extent to which individual entrepreneurs and researchers take the lead in developing innovations and starting new businesses. Yet in doing so they often harvest crops sown on fields made fertile by the government's long-term investments in research and development.[17]

CURRENT TRENDS IN FEDERAL SUPPORT

The federal government's role in supporting innovation through funding of R&D remains significant although non-federal entities have increased their share of national funding for R&D from 60 percent to 74 percent between 1990 and 2000 (see Figure 1). Federal funding still supports a substantial component, 27 percent, of the nation's total research expenditures.[18] Significantly, federal expenditures constitute 49 percent of basic research spending. In addition, federal funding for research tends to be more stable and based on a longer time horizon than funding from other sources. Commitment of federal research spending is therefore an essential component of the U.S. innovation system.

---

[14]For an excellent review of the role of government support in developing the computer industry and the Internet, see National Research Council, *Funding a Revolution: Government Support for Computing Research*, Washington, D.C.: National Academy Press, 1999.

[15]*Ibid.* See, particularly, chapter 7.

[16]See Vernon W. Ruttan, *Technology, Growth and Development: An Induced Innovation Perspective, op. cit.*

[17]David B. Audretsch and Roy Thurik, *Innovation, Industry, Evolution, and Employment*, Cambridge, UK: Cambridge University Press, 1999.

[18]See National Research Council, *Trends in Federal Support of Research and Graduate Education*, Washington, D.C.: National Academy Press, 2001, p. 4.

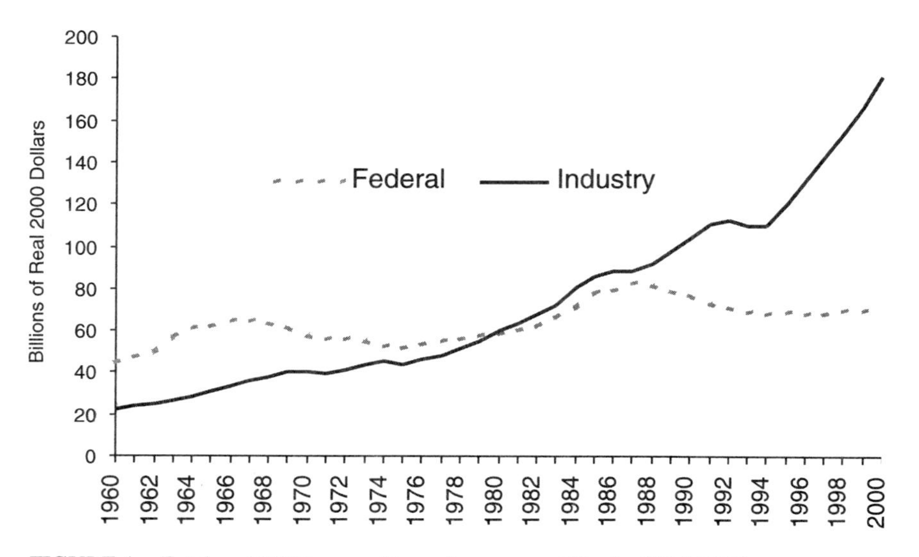

FIGURE 1 Total real R&D expenditures by source of funds, 1960-2000.
Source: U.S. National Science Foundation, National Patterns of R&D Resources.

Changing Priorities and Funding

Shifts in the composition of federal research support therefore remain important both in their own right and for the impact these shifts may have on the future development of our most innovative industries, such as biotechnology and computers, which promise to be a source of substantial innovation and growth. In both cases the role and impact of federal R&D funding is of great importance. In the case of biomedicine the promise of better health, and the tangible benefits it represents has prompted a rapid expansion of federal support for the National Institutes of Health.[19]

By the late part of the 1990s this trend had steadily gained momentum, resulting in congressional agreement to double the funding for the National Institutes of Health (NIH) over five years. This agreement has led, through two administrations, to major yearly increases in federal funding for biomedical research. This has raised concerns, even among the NIH leadership,[20] that other areas of

[19]Progress in biomedicine and drug research, the development of such diagnostic tools as magnetic resonance imaging, and the rapidly expanding understanding of the human genome give credence to this promise. Biotechnology also promises to enhance information technology. *The Economist*, "Protein Based Computer Memories, Data Harvest," December 22, 2001, reports on one possibility in this regard.

[20]See Harold Varmus, "The Impact of Physics on Biology and Medicine." Plenary talk, Centennial Meeting of the American Physical Society, Atlanta, March 22, 1999.

Box C. Federal Support of Biomedical and Information Technology Research

The source of strength in the U.S. innovation system is the diversity in its funding sources, mechanisms, and missions. While it has had many successes, it is also true that the U.S. innovation system has always had imperfections with regard to the commercialization of promising ideas.

In this context there are major challenges to achieving the promises of biomedical research. From a systemic perspective the main challenge is that the welcome increase in support for biomedical research has not been matched by increases in the supporting technologies required to effectively capitalize on the results of biomedical research. At the same time not only has support for the disciplines that drive progress in semiconductors, computers, and other key technologies not increased but has also seen reductions in real terms over a sustained period. In the view of leading figures from both the biomedical and information technology communities, this state of affairs puts at risk our ability to fully capitalize on the increasing investments in biomedical research, while equally putting at risk the economic growth that generates the revenue base for these R&D investments.

Adapted from, National Research Council, *Capitalizing on New Needs and New Opportunities: Government-Industry Partnerships in Biotechnology and Information Technologies,* C. Wessner, ed., Washington, D.C.: National Academy Press, 2002.

promising research that directly contribute to the development of medical technologies are suffering from relative neglect.[21]

As noted in Box C, shifts in federal spending for R&D are a cause for serious concern. There are two main issues: The first relates to the absolute amounts and allocations of spending. The second concerns the ability of the U.S. economy to capitalize on these investments. Each point is addressed below.

---

[21]For a discussion of these shifts, see Michael McGeary, "Recent Trends in the Federal Funding of Research and Development Related to Health and Information Technology," in National Research Council, *Capitalizing on New Needs and New Opportunities: Government-Industry Partnerships in Biotechnology and Information Technologies*, *op. cit.*

Shifts in Composition of Private Sector Research

Concerning the first point, there is a *growing concern that the United States is not investing enough and broadly enough in research and development.* In the private sector the demise of large industrial laboratories, such as IBM's Yorktown facility and Bell Laboratories, has reduced the amount of basic research conducted by private companies.[22] Hank Chesbrough, for instance, notes that large corporations "are shifting their resources away from basic discovery-oriented research to applied mission-oriented work. At the same time, ... outsourcing more of their basic research work to small startups, independent research houses and contract research organizations, while also partnering with universities and national laboratories."[23] In light of these developments, the role of partnerships gains additional relevance. Private equity markets also influence the level and distribution of investment. While the equity market in the United States is among the most dynamic in the world, it does not equally address all phases of the innovation process. In fact, current trends in the venture industry—particularly the increase in deal size—make certain types of small, early-stage financing less likely, despite the overall increase in venture funding.[24]

Although private sector R&D has steadily increased in the United States in recent years, almost all of it has been product oriented rather than geared to basic research.[25] In addition, the increase in corporate spending on research is concentrated in such sectors as the pharmaceutical industry and information technology. Within those sectors much of the R&D effort is necessarily distributed to product development, rather than to the more basic research questions.

Stagnation and Decline in Key Disciplines

The second area of concern regards the allocation of federal research funds, specifically, the *unplanned shifts in the level of federal support within the U.S.*

---

[22]See Richard Rosenbloom and William Spencer, *Engines of Innovation: U.S. Industrial Research at the End of an Era*, Boston: Harvard Business School Press, 1996.

[23]See Hank Chesbrough, "Is the Central R&D Lab Obsolete?" *Technology Review*, April 24, 2001.

[24]Venture capital funding has fallen off sharply from 1999 highs but overall fund size has increased substantially. This means that venture capital investments have recently been larger but fewer, rising from an average of $2.7 billion in 1994 to $25.4 billion in 2000. For a broad overview of the early-stage equity market for high-growth ventures in the U.S., see Jeffrey Sohl, "The Early-Stage Equity Market in the USA," *Venture Capital* 1(2): 101-20, 1999.

[25]See Charles F. Larson, "The Boom in Industry Research," *Issues in Science and Technology*, Summer 2000, p. 27. With the exception of pharmaceuticals, only a small fraction (for example, less than 4 percent in computers and semiconductors) of corporate R&D is classified as basic research. See National Research Council, *Trends in Federal Support of Research and Graduate Education,* Washington, D.C.: National Academy Press, 2001, p. 4.

public R&D portfolio. As highlighted in a recent National Research Council report,[26] the United States has experienced a largely unplanned shift in the allocation of public R&D.[27] The end of the Cold War and a political consensus to reduce the federal budget deficit has resulted in reductions in federal R&D funding in real terms for some disciplines.

In practice, for example, the decline of the defense budget corresponded with a slowdown in real terms of military support for research in physics, chemistry, mathematics, and most fields of engineering. This STEP Board study showed that in 1997 several agencies were spending substantially less on research than in 1993, even though the overall level of federal research spending was nearly the same as it was in 1993. The Department of Defense dropped 27.5 percent, the Department of the Interior was down by 13.3 percent, and the Department of Energy had declined by 5.6 percent.[28] Declines in funding for the Departments of Defense and Energy are significant because traditionally these agencies have provided the majority of federal funding for research in electrical engineering, mechanical engineering, materials engineering, physics, and computer science.[29]

After five years of stagnation federal funding for R&D did recover in FY1998. In 1999 total expenditures were up 11.7 percent over the 1993 level. These changes were driven mainly by the increases in the NIH appropriations. Breakthroughs in biotechnology and the promise of effective new medical treatments have resulted in a substantial increase in funding for the NIH, which is slated for further increases by the current administration.[30]

---

[26]See Michael McGeary, "Recent Trends in the Federal Funding of Research and Development Related to Health and Information Technology," 2002, *op. cit.*

[27]See Stephen A. Merrill and Michael McGeary, "Who's Balancing the Federal Research Portfolio and How?" *Science*, vol. 285, September 10, 1999, pp. 1679-1680. For a more recent analysis, see National Research Council, *Trends in Federal Support of Research and Graduate Education, op. cit.* For the impact of these shifts, see National Research Council, *Capitalizing on New Needs and New Opportunities: Government-Industry Partnerships in Biotechnology and Information Technologies, op. cit.*

[28]See Michael McGeary, "Recent Trends in the Federal Funding of Research and Development Related to Health and Information Technology," 2002, *op. cit.*

[29]*Ibid.*

[30]See American Association for the Advancement of Science, "AAAS Preliminary Analysis of R&D in FY 2003 Budget," February 8, 2002, <www.aaas.org/spp/R&D>. The AAAS notes that under President Bush's proposed budget "[n]on-defense R&D would increase by 7.8 percent or $3.8 billion. NIH would make up almost half of the entire non-defense R&D portfolio with another large increase, the fifth and final installment of a plan to double the NIH budget in the five years to FY2003. Excluding NIH, however, all other non-defense R&D would fall by 0.4 percent to $26.7 billion." See also, National Research Council, *Trends in Federal Support of Research and Graduate Education, op. cit.*, p. 2.

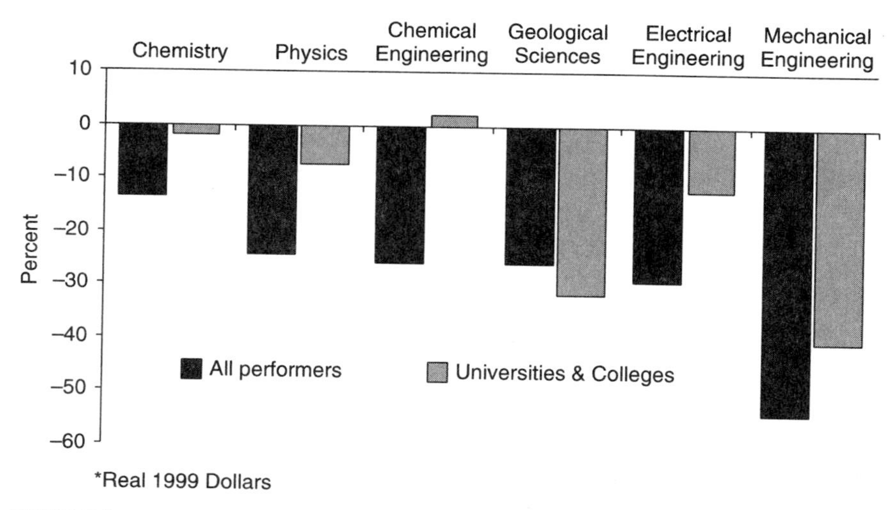

FIGURE 2 Real changes in federal obligations for research, FY1993-1999 (in real 1999 dollars).[31]

Notwithstanding this change in overall R&D funding the most recent analysis shows that even with the increase in federal research funding after 1997, the shift in the composition of federal support toward biomedical research remains largely unchanged. In 1999 the life sciences had 46 percent of federal funding for research, (see Figure 2) compared with 40 percent in 1993.[32] This difference in funding trends between the physical sciences and engineering on the one hand and the life sciences on the other hand is worrying insofar as progress in one field can depend increasingly on progress in others. Recent shifts in federal investment in research across disciplines may therefore have major consequences.

First, it will affect our ability to exploit fully the *existing* public investments in the biomedical sciences. Bringing biomedical products from the laboratory to the market is often dependent on information technology-based products and processes. Second, there is also growing concern over the cumulative impact the reduction in federal support for computing research and semiconductor technologies and the decline—over several years—in support for the disciplines that pro-

[31]The diagram shows that despite increasing (an aggregated measure) federal support for R&D to universities (e.g., ~$13.6 billion in 1995 up to ~$17.5 billion in 2000 current dollars—which is of course large enough for a real increase), these increases are unbalanced at a disaggregated level. There are, in particular, real decreases for some of the sciences that underpin many of the information technology hardware and software fields.

[32]See National Research Council, *Trends in Federal Support of Research and Graduate Education, op. cit.*, p. 2.

vide the research and students to the industry, may have for continued U.S. leadership in innovation and commercial applications in semiconductors, computers, and related applications.[33]

As we have seen, the federal government has long had a role in fostering scientific and technological progress. Yet the scope and diversity of this effort is not always fully appreciated by the general public, or often by the policy community. While support of universities and grant-making organizations—such as that by the NSF and the NIH—is well known, the important and unique roles that agencies, such as the Department of Energy and the Department of Defense, play in providing support to diverse academic disciplines and technological developments is less widely understood.[34]

In fact, the policy community has only recently begun to recognize the ramifications of these differential funding trends to the nation's continued economic growth and industrial preeminence. The committee's October 1999 conference on Government-Industry Partnerships in Biotechnology and Information Technologies helped to focus the public and policy maker attention on these concerns. The committee's subsequent report on the topics raised at the conference represent one of the first efforts to document the extent of the decline in federal support to the disciplines that many believe are necessary to realize the promise of

---

[33]See National Research Council, *Capitalizing on New Needs and New Opportunities in Biotechnology and Information Technologies*, 2002, *op. cit.*

[34]See Michael McGeary, "Recent Trends in the Federal Funding of Research and Development Related to Health and Information Technology," in National Research Council, *Capitalizing on New Needs and New Opportunities: Government-Industry Partnerships in Biotechnology and Information Technologies, op. cit.*, p. 263. McGeary notes that historically, the Departments of Defense and Energy have provided the majority of federal funding for research in electrical engineering, mechanical engineering, materials engineering, physics, and computer science. In the 1993 to 1997 period, the Administration and Congress continued to increase the budget of the NIH, which provides more than 80 percent of the federal support for the life sciences. "At the same time, they responded to the end of the Cold War by cutting the budgets of the Department of Defense and, to a lesser extent, the Department of Energy. These trends in agency funding of research have affected, in turn, research related to life sciences and IT." See also Greg Linden, David Mowery, and Rosemarie Ziedonis, "National Technology Policy in Global Markets," in Albert Link and Maryann Feldman, eds., *Innovation Policy in the Knowledge-based Economy*, Boston: Kluwer Academic Publishers, 2001, p. 312. The authors note that national laboratories, under the purview of the Department of Energy, now have extensive cooperative agreements with industrial firms in the form of Cooperative Research and Development Agreements (CRADAs). The Stevenson-Wydler Act of 1980 and the Technology Transfer Act of 1986 created this new mechanism for R&D collaboration. Amended in 1989 to allow industry-operated federal labs to participate, these laws (and high-level political interest) stimulated hundreds of CRADAs. Between 1989 and 1995 the Department of Energy alone signed more than 1,000 CRADAs. CRADAs require a high-level of technical sophistication, so that partner firms must make significant investments to support inward transfer and application of results. The last condition suggests that small firms may not be able to participate without financial and business assistance. *Ibid.*, p. 43. Funding of CRADAs declined in the late 1990s from $346 million in 1995 to an estimated $94 million in 1999, and there was a corresponding drop from 1,700 CRADAs in FY1996 to a still significant 700 in FY1999.

our investments in science and technology.[35] Box D gives a more in-depth view of the needs of strengthened investments in information technology and the opportunities for partnerships to help the nation capitalize on its investments in biomedical research.

MEETING TOMORROW'S CHALLENGES

The semiconductor industry illustrates the important role public policy on industry partnerships has played in the genesis, resurgence, and continual rapid growth of this industry.[36] The implications of current trends in the allocation of federal support, and the recognition of future technical challenges, highlight the need for expanded public support for research—often through partnerships—if the exceptional growth of the information technology industry and the extraordinary benefits related to this growth are to continue.[37]

Federal Support

Public support played a significant role in the development and growth of the computer and semiconductor industries.[38] The birth of the semiconductor industry can be dated with the invention of the first rudimentary transistor in 1947 at Bell Laboratories. Early transistor research received substantial public support; by 1952 the U.S. Army's Signal Corps Engineering Laboratory had funded 20 percent of total transistor-based research at Bell Labs.[39] The eagerness of the Defense Department to put to use this innovative and radical new technology encouraged the Army's Signal Corps to fund half of the transistor work by 1953.[40]

This public support for the then nascent semiconductor industry became more prevalent after 1955, when R&D funds were allotted to companies other than Bell. This move followed an antitrust suit, pursued by the U.S. Department of Justice that pressured Bell into sharing its patents on transistor diffusion pro-

---

[35]See National Research Council, *Capitalizing on New Needs and New Opportunities: Government-Industry Partnerships in Biotechnology and Information Technologies, op. cit.*

[36]See the Introduction to National Research Council, C. Wessner, ed., *Securing the Future: Regional and National Programs to Support the Semiconductor Industry, op.cit.*

[37]For a discussion of semiconductors and productivity, see Paul David, "Understanding Digital Technology's Evolution and the Path of Measured Productivity Growth: Present and Future in the Mirror of the Past," in E. Brynjolfsson and Brian Kahin, eds., *Understanding the Digital Economy: Data, Tools, and Research,* Cambridge, MA: MIT Press 2000, pp. 49-98. See also Jorgenson and Stiroh, 2000, *op. cit.*

[38]See National Research Council, *Funding a Revolution: Government Support for Computing Research, op.cit., passim.*

[39]See Kenneth Flamm, *Mismanaged Trade? Strategic Policy and the Semiconductor Industry,* Washington, D.C.: Brookings Institution Press, 1996, pp. 30-31.

[40]*Ibid.*

cesses.[41] Some estimates show, that between the late 1950s and early 1970s, the federal government directly or indirectly funded up to 40 percent to 45 percent of industrial R&D in the semiconductor industry.[42] On the demand side, federal consumption dominated the market for integrated circuits (ICs). ICs, for example, found their first major military application in the Minuteman II guided missile. Throughout the 1960s, military requirements were complemented by the needs of the Apollo space program.[43]

The Competitive Challenge of the 1980s

While the U.S. government was quick to provide early funding to promote the development of semiconductors for both military and space exploration programs,[44] its subsequent role in assisting the commercial semiconductor sector was much more restrained. Meanwhile, governments abroad were more purposeful in supporting their domestic semiconductor industries. The Japanese government, for example, recognizing the country's position as a late entrant in semiconductors, instituted policy measures to jump-start its industry in the 1970s. Under the guidance of the Ministry of International Trade and Industry (MITI) the country made a systematic effort to promote a vibrant domestic semiconductor industry.[45] The vertically integrated structure of Japanese industry appeared to provide major advantages with respect to the capital-intensive investments required for manufacturing facilities. Japanese firms undertook a massive capacity build-up in the early 1980s, accelerating their gains in market share through aggressive price cutting. The total DRAM market share of U.S. industry sank from roughly 90 percent in the late 1970s to less than 10 percent by 1984-1985, with many U.S. firms exiting the DRAM market entirely.[46] The dramatic impact of the Japanese competition led many informed U.S. observers to question the future viability of the U.S. semiconductor industry.[47]

---

[41]*Ibid.*

[42]*Ibid.*

[43]For an overview of the government's early role in the semiconductor industry, and its contributions over time see Ken Flamm, *Mismanaged Trade? Strategic Policy and the Semiconductor Industry, op. cit.* pp. 1-38. Government procurement enabled U.S. firms to improve yield and efficiency through volume production and encouraged wider application of IC technology, first in military and then in commercial technologies. National Bureau of Standards, *The Influence of Defense Procurement and Sponsorship of Research and Development on the Development of the Civilian Electronics Industry*, June 30, 1977.

[44]See Laura Tyson, *Who's Bashing Whom? Trade Conflict in High Technology Industries*, Washington, D.C.: IIE, 1992.

[45]*Ibid.* Tyson presents a partial list of joint research and development projects in microelectronics sponsored by MITI.

[46]*Ibid.*

[47]*Ibid.* pp. 85-113. Tyson provides an excellent analysis of the competition for dominance in the semiconductor industry. See also Kenneth Flamm, *Mismanaged Trade? Strategic Policy in the Semiconductor Industry, op. cit.*

Box D. Key Findings and Recommendations of the Committee for Government-Industry Partnerships in Biotechnology and Information Technologies

The Committee's report on *Capitalizing on New Needs and New Opportunities: Government-Industry Partnerships in Biotechnology and Information Technologies,* addresses a topic of fundamental policy concern. To capture the benefits of substantial U.S. investments in biomedical R&D, parallel investments in a wide range of seemingly unrelated disciplines are also required. This element of the Committee's analysis draws attention to the fall-off in R&D investments in science and engineering needed to sustain the growth of the U.S. economy and to capitalize on the rapidly growing federal investments in biomedicine. It calls for greater support for interdisciplinary training to support such new areas as bioinformatics and urges more emphasis on and support for multidisciplinary research centers.

Among its central findings

Information Technology and *Biotechnology Are Key Sectors for the Twenty-first Century.* Advances in information technologies remain central to economic growth; they will also be critical to progress in the biotechnology revolution itself. At the same time, progress in biotechnology is increasingly dependent on the pace of advances in information technology.

Multidisciplinary Approaches Are Increasingly Needed in Science and Engineering Research. Complex research problems require the integration of both people and new knowledge across a range of disciplines. In turn this requires knowledge workers with interdisciplinary training in mathematics, computer science, and biology.

Government-Industry and University-Industry Partnerships Have Often Been Effective in Supporting the Development of New Technologies. Partnerships that have often provided effective support include the engineering research centers and science and technology centers funded by the NSF, the National Institute of Standards and Technology's ATP program, and the Department of Defense's former Technology Reinvestment program. They also included activities funded by cooperative research and development agreements (CRADAs). In addition, SEMATECH, initially government and industry funded, has played a key role in improving manufacturing technologies for the U.S. semiconductor industry.

Federal R&D Funding and Other Innovation Policies Have Been Important in Supporting the Development of U.S. Industrial Capabilities in Computing and Biotechnology. The history of the U.S. biotechnology and computing sectors illustrates the value of sustained federal support.

Limitations of Venture Capital. While the U.S. venture capital market—the largest and best developed in the world—often plays a crucial role in the formation of new high-technology companies, the provision of venture capital, with its informed assessment and management oversight, is but one element of a larger innovation system. It is not a substitute for government support of long-term scientific and technological research.

Key recommendations of the committee

- Government and industry should expand support of research partnerships and other cooperative arrangements within and among sectors (government, industry, university, and non-profit) and take other steps to facilitate multidisciplinary research leading to advances in biotechnology and information technology.
- The scientific community, U.S. industry, and the federal government should explicitly examine the implications of recent shifts in the allocation of federal investment among fields (especially the decline in federal funding for research in the physical sciences and engineering) and address possible solutions.
- Federal policy makers should support an infrastructure and create an environment conducive to research partnerships and other cooperative arrangements. Such an environment can be facilitated, for example, through building interdisciplinary competence in multidisciplinary research, increased support for interdisciplinary training of graduate students, and a review of the impact of patent decisions on technological progress.

Adapted from, National Research Council, *Capitalizing on New Needs and New Opportunities: Government-Industry Partnerships in Biotechnology and Information Technologies,* C. Wessner, ed., Washington, D.C.: National Academy Press, 2002.

The Policy Response

In response to intense competition from the Japanese producers, the U.S. industry launched a series of initiatives, some independently (e.g., the Semiconductor Research Corporation). As the crisis deepened, the industry concluded it needed to cooperate with the government, first to stop what it considered to be unfair trade practices by Japanese producers, and later to strengthen its domestic capabilities.[48] The range of these initiatives was extensive. They included:

- Founding of the Semiconductor Research Corporation (1982);
- Creation of the U.S.-Japan Working Group on High Technology (1983);
- Passage of the National Cooperative Research Act (1984);
- Passage of the Trade and Tariff Act (1984);
- Passage of the Semiconductor Chip Protection Act (1984);
- Signing of the Semiconductor Trade Agreement by the United States and Japan (1986);
- Founding of SEMATECH (1987);
- Congressional approval of the formation of the National Advisory Committee on Semiconductors (1988);
- Renewal of the Semiconductor Trade Agreement (1990); and
- Beginning of the Semiconductor Roadmap process (1992).

Efforts to address issues in U.S. manufacturing quality (see below) proceeded in parallel with efforts to resolve questions about Japan's trading practices. A series of trade agreements between Japan and the United States did not resolve trade frictions between the two countries, nor did the agreements redress the steadily declining U.S. market share. [49] At the urging of the industry, the federal government took several significant policy initiatives designed to support the U.S. semiconductor industry.

Following a series of unsatisfactory trade agreements, there was a significant shift in U.S. policy on trade in semiconductors, notably through the conclusion of

[48]For a first-hand discussion of the U.S. concerns and the trade negotiations during this period, see Clyde Prestowitz, *Trading Places*, New York: Basic Books, 1988. See also Thomas R. Howell, Alan Wm. Wolff, Brent L. Bartlett, and R. Michael Gadbaw, *Conflict Among Nations: Trade Policies in the 1990s, op. cit.*

[49]For an industry perspective, see the account by Charles E. Sporck (with Richard L. Molay), *Spinoff: A Personal History of the Industry that Changed the World*, Sarnac Lake, New York: Sarnac Lake Publishing, 2001. Sporck recounts that, in this period, when memory products (DRAMs) represented a major percentage of the industry, "the core strategy of the Japanese industry was to add manufacturing capacity at a pace unrelated to market share" and to price products below U.S. producers. p. 244.

the 1986 Semiconductor Trade Agreement (STA) with Japan.[50] The agreement sought to improve access to the Japanese market for U.S. producers and to end dumping (selling products below cost) in U.S. and other markets.[51] After President Reagan's decision to impose trade sanctions, the STA brought an end to the dumping in the U.S. and other markets and succeeded in obtaining limited access to the Japanese market for foreign producers, in particular, Korean and later Taiwanese DRAM producers.[52]

A second major step was the industry's decision to seek a partnership between the government and a coalition of like-minded private firms to form the SEMATECH consortium, whose purpose was to revive a seriously weakened U.S. industry through collaborative research and pooling of manufacturing knowledge.[53] A central element of the challenges facing the U.S. Semiconductor industry was manufacturing quality. By the mid-1980s, the leading U.S. semiconductor firms had recognized the strategic importance of quality and began to initiate quality improvement programs. A key element in this effort was the formation of

---

[50]See Clyde Prestowitz, *Trading Places*, *op.cit.* and Thomas R. Howell, Alan Wm. Wolff, Brent L. Bartlett, and R. Michael Gadbaw, *Conflict Among Nations: Trade Policies in the 1990s, op.cit.*. For additional discussion of the Semiconductor Trade Agreement, see National Research Council, *Conflict and Cooperation in National Competition for High-Technology Industry, op. cit.* pp. 132-41. For a discussion of dumping/anti-dumping trade-policy debate, see pp. 82-87.

[51]As part of the agreement, dumping suits in the U.S. and the Section 301 case were suspended in return for agreement to improve market access and terminate dumping. A side letter called for a twenty percent market share for foreign firms within five years. Laura Tyson, *Who's Bashing Whom? Trade Conflict in High Technology Industries, op. cit.*, p. 109.

[52]For a discussion of the impact of the agreement, see K. Flamm, *Mismanaged Trade? Strategic Policy and the Semiconductor Industry, op. cit.* For an earlier assessment see, Laura Tyson, *Who's Bashing Whom? Trade Conflict in High Technology Industries, op. cit.*, pp. 136-143. As Laura Tyson points out, the trade agreement was a first in many respects. It was the first major U.S. trade agreement focused on an advanced technology, and the first one motivated by concerns about the loss of competitiveness rather than the loss of employment. It was unusual in that the agreement concentrated on improving market access abroad rather than restricting access to the U.S. market. And unlike other bilateral trade deals, it sought to regulate trade (i.e., end dumping) not only in trade between the United States and Japan but in other global markets as well. It also included, for the first time, the threat of trade sanctions should the agreement not be respected. As such, it signaled a significant shift in U.S. trade policy. *Ibid*, p. 109.

[53]As noted, the semiconductor manufacturers—secretive, often adversarial competitors—faced an early critical challenge to effective cooperation within SEMATECH in the fear that cooperation would reveal proprietary secrets to competitors. As Larry Browning and Judy Shetler note in their comprehensive study of the consortium, this initial reluctance centered around three questions: "What technology could they use for the mission of improving performance?" "What firm would they want to contribute a cutting-edge proprietary process?" and "What would be the use in working on anything else?" See Larry D. Browning and Judy C. Shetler, *SEMATECH: Saving the U.S. Semiconductor Industry,* College Station: Texas A&M University Press, 2000, p. 22.

the consortium, which in part reflected the belief that the Japanese cooperative programs had been instrumental in the success of Japanese producers.[54]

The SEMATECH consortium represented a significant new experiment for government-industry cooperation in technology development. Conceived and funded under the Reagan administration, the consortium represented an unusual collaborative effort, both for the U.S. government and for the fiercely competitive U.S. semiconductor industry.[55] The Silicon Valley entrepreneurs hesitated about cooperating with each other and were even more hesitant about cooperating with the government—an attitude mirrored in some quarters in Washington.[56]

Industry Leadership

From the outset, the industry took a leading role in setting its objectives, managing its resources, and measuring its accomplishments.[57] The consortium showed substantial flexibility in its early years as its members and leadership struggled to define where it could make the maximum impact. After an early focus on developing a manufacturing facility to help solve production problems (rather than rely on a lab), the consortium eventually focused on three goals which involved improving:

- Manufacturing processes;
- Factory management; and
- Industry infrastructure, especially the supply base of equipment and materials.[58]

---

[54]See Larry D. Browning and Judy C. Shetler, *SEMATECH, Saving the U.S. Semiconductor Industry, op. cit.*, Chapter 1, p. vv.

[55]As Hedrick Smith noted "the mere formation of SEMATECH required a radically new mind-set at some of America's leading high-tech corporations." See Hedrick Smith, *Rethinking America*, New York: Random House, 1995, p. 385. In particular, Charlie Sporck, then CEO of National Semiconductor, and Bob Noyce, Intel Co-founder, played a decisive role in garnering the political and industrial support for the formation of the consortium.

[56]See Larry D. Browning and Judy C. Shetler, *SEMATECH, Saving the U.S. Semiconductor Industry, op. cit*, pp. 21-23. Browning and Shetler record that the Treasury and Council of Economic Advisors were adamantly opposed to government funding of a consortium; the Departments of Defense and Commerce were supportive. *Ibid*, p. 24.

[57]SEMATECH's industry-driven structure and innovative management approach to identifying and achieving its objectives have been credited with contributing to its effectiveness. See Larry D. Browning and Judy C. Shetler, *SEMATECH: Saving the U.S. Semiconductor Industry, op. cit.*, p. 206, 210. Defense officials were closely consulted on technical direction, then the consortium management was left in charge of implementation. A similar observation about SEMATECH's flexible approach is made in Peter Grindley, David C. Mowery, and Brian Silverman, "SEMATECH and Collaborative Research: Lessons in the Design of High-Technology Consortia," *Journal of Policy Analysis and Management*, 13(4), 1996.

[58]See Larry D. Browning and Judy C. Shetler, *SEMATECH, Saving the U.S. Semiconductor Industry, op. cit*, p. 205.

The formation of SEMATECH thus provided an opportunity to bring together leading U.S. producers to focus initially on product quality. During this period, the U.S. industry also increased its capital expenditure and improved its ability to manage the development and introduction of new process technologies into high-volume manufacturing.[59] The industry was aided in this process through its collaboration on common challenges under the auspices of SEMATECH.

The Impact of SEMATECH

While many factors affected the recovery of the U.S. industry, the public policy initiatives in trade and cooperative research were key among elements in the industry's revival—contributing respectively to the restoration of financial health and product quality.[60] The stronger performance of U.S. producers was revealed in gains in global market share that rested in part on improvements in product quality and manufacturing process yields, areas in which SEMATECH played a contributing role. As Flamm and Wang observe, though there are "a few vocal exceptions," SEMATECH has been credited, *within the industry*, as playing some part in the "resurgence among U.S. semiconductor producers in the 1990s."[61] Perhaps the most compelling affirmation of the value of the consortium is the willingness of most of SEMATECH's corporate members to continue participating in the consortium and to continue with this cooperation even after federal funding ceased.[62] Other economists knowledgeable about the industry reach similar conclusions. For example, Macher, Mowery, and Hodges note that continued industry participation represents "a strong signal that industry managers believe that the consortium has produced important benefits."[63]

---

[59]*Ibid*, p. 262. See also D.C. Mowery and N. Hatch, "Managing the Development and Introduction of New Manufacturing Processes in the Global Semiconductor Industry," in G. Dosi, R. Nelson, and S. Winter, eds., *The Nature and Dynamics of Organizational Capabilities*, New York: Oxford University Press, 2002.

[60]See Jeffrey T. Macher, David C. Mowery, and David A. Hodges, "Semiconductors," *op. cit.* pp. 266-267 and 277.

[61]See Kenneth Flamm and Qifei Wang, *Sematech Revisited: Assessing Consortium Impacts on Semiconductor Industry R&D.* in this volume. Economists share this view. As Flamm notes, "Economists generally view the program as the preeminent model of a cooperative government-industry joint R&D venture." See the presentation by Kenneth Flamm in National Research Council, *Regional and National Programs to Support the Semiconductor Industry, op cit.* For the views of a frequent critic, see T.J. Rodgers, "Silicon Valley Versus Corporate Welfare," *CATO Institute Briefing Papers*, Briefing Paper No. 37, April 27, 1998.

[62]At a meeting in 1994, The SEMATECH Board of Directors reasoned that the U.S. semiconductor industry had regained strength in both the device-making and supplier markets, and thus voted to seek an end to matching federal funding after 1996. For a brief timeline and history of SEMATECH, see <http://www.sematech.org/public/corporate/history/history.htm>.

[63]See Jeffrey T. Macher, David C. Mowery, and David A. Hodges, "Semiconductors," *op. cit.*, p. 272.

Perspectives from Abroad

The positive perception of the consortium has influenced the creation and structure of consortia abroad. Kenneth Flamm points out that the consortium is perceived as a success in Japan, directly influencing the formation and design of the ASET and SELETE programs (see Box B).[64] SEMATECH appears also to have had a similar influence on the initiation and operation of European programs such as MEDEA and IMEC.[65]

An informed perspective on the positive model of the U.S. partnership is offered by Hitachi's Toshiaki Masuhara who observes that there has been a good balance of support in the United States by government and industry for research through the universities. This has included "a very good balance between design and processing." He adds that the overall success of U.S. industry appears to have come from the contributions of five overlapping efforts. These include:

- The SIA roadmap to determine the direction of research;
- Planning of resource allocation by SIA and SRC;
- Allocation of federal funding through Department of Defense, National Science Foundation, and the Defense Advanced Research Projects Agency;
- The success of SEMATECH and International SEMATECH in supporting research on process, technology, design, and testing; and
- The Focus Center Research Project.[66]

In addition to these informed opinions, the willingness of new firms such as Infineon (Germany), Philips (the Netherlands), and ST Thompson (France) to join International SEMATECH is a further affirmation of the perceived value of the consortium's research and related activities.

---

[64]As a leading Japanese industrialist observed, "A major factor contributing to the U.S. semiconductor industry's recovery from this perilous situation [in the 1980s] was a U.S. national policy based around cooperation between industry, government, and academia." Hajime Susaki, Chairman of NEC Corporation, "Japanese Semiconductor Industry's Competitiveness: LSI Industry in Jeopardy," *Nikkei Microdevices*, December 2000.

[65]IMEC, headquartered in Leuven, Belgium, is Europe's leading independent research center for the development and licensing of microelectronics, and information and communication technologies (ICT). IMEC's activities concentrate on design of integrated information and communication systems; silicon process technology; silicon technology and device integration; microsystems, components and packaging; and advanced training in microelectronics. For more information on IMEC, see <http://www.imec.be/>. SEMATECH was emulated in the U.S. as well. For example, NEMI (The National Electronics Manufacturing Initiative) was formed in 1993 to focus on strategic electronic components and electronics manufacturing systems. NEMI is an industry-led consortium with fifty members.

[66]See the presentation by Toshiaki Masuhara in National Research Council, *Regional and National Programs to Support the Semiconductor Industry, op cit.*

These positive views from leading figures in the industry, in both the U.S. and abroad, underscore Flamm and Wang's observation that SEMATECH was thought to be a "privately productive and worthwhile activity."[67] Researchers such as Macher, Mowery, and Hodges, support Flamm, finding that "government initiatives, ranging from trade policy to financial support to university research and R&D consortia, played a role in the industry's revival," while adding, as do Flamm and Wang, that the "specific links between undertakings such as SEMATECH and improved manufacturing performance are difficult to measure."[68] Challenges of measurement notwithstanding, those most closely involved (i.e. leading figures in the industry) are thus positive in their overall assessment of the consortium.[69]

A Positive Policy Framework

This unprecedented level of cooperation, and the important corresponding collaborative activity among the semiconductor materials and equipment suppliers, thus appear to have contributed to a resurgence in the quality of U.S. products and indirectly to the resurgence of the industry.[70] The collective accomplishments and impact of the consortium may well have been an essential element contributing to the recovery of the U.S. industry, though it should be underscored that its contribution and other public policy initiatives were by no means suffi-

---

[67]See Kenneth Flamm and Qifei Wang, *Sematech Revisited: Assessing Consortium Impacts on Semiconductor industry R&D, op. cit.*

[68]See Jeffrey T. Macher, David C. Mowery, and David A. Hodges, "Semiconductors," *op. cit.*, p. 247.

[69]There are corporate critics of SEMATECH. T.J. Rodgers of Cypress Semiconductors is a frequent critic. For a comprehensive statement of his views, see "Silicon Valley Versus Corporate Welfare," *CATO Institute Briefing Papers*, Briefing Paper No. 37, April 27, 1998. Rodgers notes that "My battles with Sematech started when our engineers were denied access to an advanced piece of wafer-making equipment, a chemical-mechanical polisher (CMP) machine manufactured by an Arizona company [that]...SEMATECH [had] contracted...to develop....Cypress was denied access to that critical piece of wafer-making equipment, which could have differentiated between winners and losers in the next-generation technology. At that point I became a vocal critic of SEMATECH ...." (p. 9). Rodgers also objected to the SEMATECH dues structure, finding the $1 million minimum to be onerous for a relatively small semiconductor-producing firm. He adds "I believe that if SEMATECH had been formed as a private consortium with a smaller budget, it would have come to its current, more efficient model of operation much more quickly." (p. 10).

[70]As a research consortium, SEMATECH's contributions were necessarily indirect. As Browning and Shetler observe, "any effects caused by SEMATECH would, of course, be indirect because as a member firm, executives are disposed to point out, it was ultimately the member companies' factory production that led to the increased U.S. semiconductor market share. SEMATECH's role has been to develop new manufacturing technologies and methods and transfer them to its member companies, which in turn manufacture and sell improved chips. SEMATECH's precise contribution to the market recovery is therefore difficult to directly assess." See Larry Browning and Judy Shetler, *SEMATECH: Saving the U.S. Semiconductor Industry, op. cit.*, p. 208.

cient to ensure the industry's recovery. Essentially, these public policy initiatives can be understood as having *collectively* provided positive framework conditions for private action by U.S. semiconductor producers.[71]

Technical Challenges, Competitive Challenges, and Capacity Constraints

For more than 30 years the growth of the semiconductor industry has been largely associated with the ability of researchers to shrink the transistor steadily and quickly and thereby increase its speed, without commensurate increases in costs (Moore's Law). If Moore's Law is indeed to be maintained, then a continuation of productivity increases will likely depend on the ongoing benefits associated with the process of "scaling" in microelectronics.[72] There are, however, physical limits to miniaturization, including odd and undesirable quantum effects that appear under extreme miniaturization.[73]

The semiconductor industry also faces the challenge of soaring chip-manufacturing costs. When Intel was founded in 1968, a single machine used to produce semiconductor chips cost roughly $12,000. Today a chip-fabricating plant costs billions of dollars, and the expense is expected to continue to rise as chips become ever more complex. Adding to this concern is the realization that capital costs are rising far faster than revenue.[74] In 2000, for example, average total expenditures for a six-inch equivalent "wafer" were $3,110, an increase of 117 percent over the average total costs for a six-inch wafer in 1989, and a 390 percent increase since 1978.[75]

---

[71]Many factors contributed to the recovery of the U.S. industry. It is unlikely that any one factor would have proved sufficient independently. Trade policy, no matter how innovative, could not have met the requirement to improve U.S. product quality. On the other hand, by their long-term nature, even effective industry-government partnerships can be rendered useless in a market unprotected against dumping by foreign rivals. Most importantly, neither trade nor technology policy can succeed in the absence of adaptable, adequately capitalized, effectively managed, technologically innovative companies.

[72]See Bill Spencer's discussion of semiconductors in: *Measuring and Sustaining the New Economy, op. cit.*

[73]See Paul A. Packan, "Pushing the Limits: Integrated Circuits Run into Limits Due to Transistors," *Science,* September 24, 1999. Packan notes that "these fundamental issues have not previously limited the scaling of transistors and represent a considerable challenge for the semiconductor industry. There are currently no known solutions to these problems. To continue the performance trends of the past 20 years and maintain Moore's Law of improvement will be the most difficult challenge the semiconductor industry has ever faced."

[74]See Charles C. Mann, "The End of Moore's Law?" *Technology Review*, May/June 2000, at <http://www.technologyreview.com/magazine/may00/mann.asp>.

[75]These statistics originate from the Semiconductor Industry Association's *2001 Annual Databook: Review of Global and U.S. Semiconductor Competitive Trends, 1978-2000*. A wafer is a thinly sliced (less than 1 millimeter) circular piece of semiconductor material that is used to make semiconductor devices and integrated circuits.

The consensus in the engineering community is that improvements, both large and small, will continue to uphold Moore's Law for another decade or so, even as scaling brings the industry very close to the theoretical minimum size of silicon-based circuits.[76] To the extent that physical constraints or cost pressures limit the continued growth of the industry they will necessarily influence the role of the industry in stimulating productivity growth in the broader economy. As capital costs rise, as worldwide fabrication capacity increases, and as alternative business models (such as the foundry system) gain prominence, the competitive position of U.S. firms may be challenged.[77]

The unprecedented technical challenges faced by the industry underscore the need for talented individuals—the architects of the future—to devise new solutions to these technical challenges.[78] The simple and perhaps alarming fact is that this pool of available skilled and qualified labor is shrinking. Historically the U.S. government has supported human resources through its system of funding basic research at universities, whereby the work and training of graduate students and postdoctoral scholars are supported by research grants to principal investigators. However, the rapid growth in demand for skilled engineers, scientists, and technicians is creating challenges on several fronts.

This trend has been aggravated in recent years by the steep decline in federal funding for university research in the sciences relevant to information technologies, such as mathematics, physics, and engineering. As we noted in the previous section, these declines are the unintended result of unplanned shifts in the level of federal support within the U.S. public R&D portfolio.

Challenges to U.S. Public Policy

While federal funding for SEMATECH ended after 1996 at the industry's initiation, the debate has continued in Congress and succeeding administrations as to whether and to what extent the U.S. government should continue to invest federal funds in supporting R&D in microelectronics.[79] Some observers argue

---

[76]See discussion by Bob Doering of Texas Instruments on "Physical Limits of Silicon CMOS and Semiconductor Roadmap Predictions," in *Measuring and Sustaining the New Economy, op. cit.*

[77]See remarks by George Scalise, President of the Semiconductor Industry Association, at the Symposium *Productivity and Cyclicality in the Semiconductor Industry*, organized by Harvard University.

[78]David Tennenhouse, Vice-president and Director of Research and Development at Intel, emphasized this point in his presentation at the joint Strategic Assessments Group and Defense Advanced Research Projects Agency conference *The Global Computer Industry Beyond Moore's Law: A Technical, Economic, and National Security Perspective,* January 14-15, 2002, Herndon, VA.

[79]At a meeting in 1994 the SEMATECH Board of Directors reasoned that the U.S. semiconductor industry had regained strength in both the device-making and supplier markets, and voted to seek an end to matching federal funding after 1996. For a brief timeline and history of SEMATECH, see <http://www.sematech.org/public/corporate/history/history.htm>.

that the role of the government should be curtailed, asserting that federal programs in microelectronics represent "corporate welfare."[80] Advocates of R&D cooperation among universities, industry, and government to advance knowledge and the nation's capacity to produce microelectronics argue that such support is justified, not only for this technology's relevance to many national missions (not least defense), but also for its benefits to the national economy and society as a whole.[81]

In fact, no consensus exists on this point or on appropriate mechanisms or levels of support for research. Discussions of the need for such programs have often been dogged by doctrinaire views as to the appropriateness of government support for industry R&D and domestic politics (e.g., balancing the federal budget) that have generated uncertainty about this form of cooperation, especially at the federal level.[82]

An effect of this irresolution has been a passive federal role in addressing the technical uncertainties central to the continued rapid evolution of information technologies. DARPA's annual funding of microelectronics R&D—the principal channel of direct federal financial support—has declined, and is projected to decline further (See Figure 3).[83] As noted above, this trend runs counter to those in Europe and East Asia, where governments are providing substantial direct and indirect funding in this sector. The declines in U.S. federal funding for research are of particular concern to U.S. industry.

---

[80]See T.J. Rodgers, "Silicon Valley Versus Corporate Welfare," *op. cit.*

[81]Policy debates on public-private partnerships have often suffered from sloganeering, with no clear resolution. One side claims that the market is efficient and will therefore sort itself out without the involvement of government. The other side counters that markets are imperfect and that, in any event, government missions cannot depend on markets alone, nor wait for the appropriate price signals to emerge. Therefore public policy has a role—and always has. The contribution of this analysis, and others in the series, is to document current cooperative activity and redirect attention away from this abstract rhetoric and demonstrate that carefully crafted partnerships can help accelerate innovation.

[82]See David M. Hart, *Forged Consensus: Science, Technology, and Economic Policy in the United States,* 1921-1953, Princeton: Princeton University Press, 1998, p. 230. For a broader review of these differing perspectives, see Richard Bingham, *Industrial Policy American Style: From Hamilton to HDTV,* New York: M.E. Sharpe, 1998. See also I. Lebow, *Information Highways and Byways: From the Telegraph to the 21st Century,* New York: Institute of Electrical and Electronics Engineers, 1995. For a global perspective, see J. Fallows, *Looking into the Sun: The Rise of the New East Asian Economic and Political System,* New York: Pantheon Books, 1994; and J.A. Brander and B.J. Spencer, "International R&D Rivalry and Industrial Strategy," *Review of Economic Studies,* 50(4):707-722, 1983. There is much less ambivalence at the state level. See Christopher Coburn and Dan Berglund, *Partnerships: A Compendium of State and Federal Cooperative Technology Programs.* Columbus, OH: Battelle Press, 1995.

[83]This presentation understates the declines. Support for lithography, for example, fell from $54.4 million in FY2001 to $32.6 in FY2002 and is projected to stabilize at $25 million in FY2003. Some reports suggest that overall support for microelectronics research actually fell from about $350 mil-

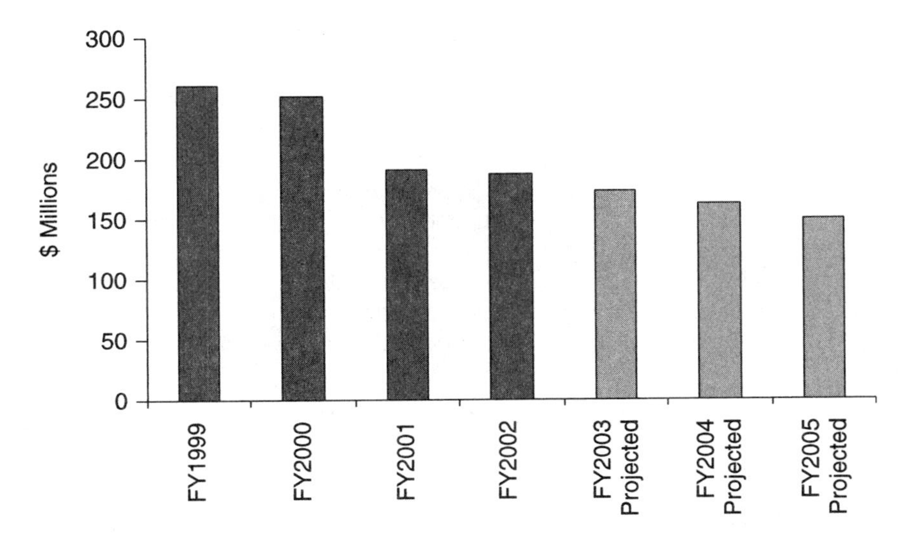

FIGURE 3 Defense Advanced Research Projects Agency's annual funding of microelectronics R&D. SOURCE: DARPA 2001-05 President's Budget R-1 Exhibit

Addressing the R&D Gap: The Focus Center Programs

Reflecting this concern, the industry has initiated several new programs to strengthen the research capability of U.S. universities. The largest of these is the Focus Center Research program (FCRP), through which the U.S. semiconductor industry, the federal government, and universities work cooperatively on cutting-edge research deemed critical to the continued growth of the industry. This program is operated by the Semiconductor Research Corporation, which funds and operates university-based research centers in microelectronics.[84] In cooperation with the government and leading universities, the industry plans to eventually establish six national focus centers and channel $60 million per year into new research activities. However, the recent sharp downturn in the industry has put in question this commitment.

---

lion in the early 1990s to about $55 million in 2000. See Scott Nance, "Broad Federal Research Required to Keep Semiconductors on Track," *New Technology Week,* October 30, 2000. Sonny Maynard, Semiconductor Research Corporation, cited in presentation by Dr. Michael Polcari, "Current Challenges: A U.S. and Global Perspective," National Research Council, *Symposium on National Programs to Support the Semiconductor Industry* (October 2000).

[84]The FCRP is part of MARCO, the Microelectronics Advanced Research Corporation within the Semiconductor Research Corporation (SRC). See MARCO Web site, <http://marco.fcrp.org>. MARCO has its own management personnel but uses the infrastructure and resources of the SRC.

In addition, International SEMATECH continues to promote greater cooperation among major firms and now includes international members, though this initiative appears to have been set back by the recent downturn in the industry. Still, there are some promising signs. The most recent budgets for the NSF and the Department of Defense include increases in some important semiconductor areas that had been reduced during the 1990s. These developments only emphasize the limitations of private-sector support, the risks of lag effects in the R&D pipeline, and the disconnect between research needs and resources.

These industry-university initiatives are valuable and merit additional support. The committee accordingly believes it is important to increase support for basic research in the sciences related to information technologies.[85]

MEETING NEW CHALLENGES—COUNTERING TERRORISM

For the current war on terrorism, partnerships have a demonstrated capacity to marshal the ingenuity of industry to meet new needs for national security. Because they are flexible and can be organized on an *ad hoc* basis, partnerships are an effective means to focus diverse expertise and innovative technologies rapidly to help counter new threats. As a recent report of the National Academy of Sciences notes, "For the government and private sector to work together on increasing homeland security, effective public-private partnerships and cooperative projects must occur. There are many models for government-industry collaboration—cooperative research and development agreements, the NIST Advanced Technology Program, and the Small Business Research Innovation Program, to cite a few."[86]

Indeed, programs such as SBIR are being harnessed to bring new technologies to address urgent national missions. For example, the National Institute of Allergies and Infectious Diseases at the National Institutes of Health has rapidly expanded its efforts in support of research on possible bio-terrorism in response to recent threats and attacks. Specifically, NIAID has expanded research and development countermeasures—including vaccines, therapeutics, and diagnostic tests—needed to counter and control the release of agents of bio-terrorism.[87]

Appropriately structured partnerships can also serve as a policy instrument that aligns the incentives of private firms to achieve national missions without compelling them to do so. As the National Academy of Sciences report cited above further notes, "A more effective approach is to give the private sector the

[85]See National Research Council, *Capitalizing on New Needs and New Opportunities: Government-Industry Partnerships in Biotechnology and Information Technologies*, *op. cit.*

[86]National Research Council, *Making the Nation Safer—The Role of Science and Technology in Countering Terrorism. op. cit.*, 2002.

[87]See NIAID FY2003 Budget Justification Narrative at *<http://www.niaid.nih.gov/director/congress/2002/cj >*.

widest possible latitude for innovation and, where appropriate, to design R&D strategies in which commercial uses of technologies rest on a common base of investment. Companies then have the potential to address vulnerabilities while increasing the robustness of public and private infrastructure against unintended and natural failures, improving the reliability of systems and quality of service, and in some cases, increasing productivity."

Dual-use strategies can play key roles in meeting critical short-term mission goals, as well as in developing over the longer term, more effective and lower-cost technologies.[88] Additionally, joint interagency design and execution programs—with a single source of funds and joint decisions on each dollar to be spent—constitute one approach to address critically important national initiatives collaboratively. Partnerships, when properly structured and managed, can achieve more positive results than separately channeled funding.

[88]The case of the Technology Reinvestment Project (TRP) illustrates the potential for positive collaborations between defense contractors and commercial firms for dual-use technology development. See J. Stowsky, "Politics and Policy: The Technology Reinvestment Program and the Dilemmas of Dual Use," Mimeo, University of California. See also Linda R. Cohen, "Dual-Use and the Technology Reinvestment Project," in *Investing in Innovation*, Lewis M. Branscomb and James H. Keller, eds., Cambridge, MA: MIT Press, 1999.

V

THE ROLE OF PARTNERSHIPS IN CURRENT TECHNOLOGY POLICY

The Role of Partnerships in Current Technology Policy

THE RELEVANCE OF PARTNERSHIPS

Partnerships in general are cooperative relationships involving government, industry, laboratories, and (increasingly) universities organized to encourage innovation and commercialization. The long-term goal of these public-private partnerships is to develop industrial processes, products, and services, and thereby, apply new knowledge to government missions such as improved health, environmental protection, and national security.

The Roles of Partnerships

Partnerships can take many forms, though they most often involve direct support for or participation in research and development (R&D) carried out among these entities. They can represent a pragmatic response to particular market situations in which firms and other organizations for a variety of interrelated reasons are unlikely to undertake needed investments in R&D independently.

- **Funding New Ideas**

  Partnerships can help overcome funding gaps for needed R&D and for new products. In the real world, new innovative firms face substantial obstacles in their search for equity finance.[1] Even though venture capital-

[1]See Joshua Lerner, "Public Venture Capital: Rationale and Evaluation," in National Research Council, *The Small Business Innovation Research Program, Challenges and Opportunities,* C. Wessner, ed., Washington, D.C.: National Academy Press, 1999, Appendix A.

ists have strong motivations to gather information about the small businesses in which they may be investing, the idea entrepreneur is often the only person with in-depth knowledge of the market potential of the new technology.[2] As Roger Noll notes, "Informational problems give rise to a second rationale for public support for commercial R&D, which is to improve efficiency in the market for investment in R&D-intensive firms, especially startups. The basic problem here is that people with innovative ideas may lack financial capital to undertake the R&D necessary to commercialize their innovation, and those with funds available for investment may be uninformed about the ideas."[3]

The challenge facing new businesses in attracting adequate funding to nurture ideas through the innovation process can be complicated further by the cyclicality and herding tendencies of the financial markets.

- **Training Researchers**

Partnerships can play a supportive role in developing the researchers with the skills needed for modern collaborative research and development. R&D today increasingly calls for researchers who can integrate knowledge across traditional disciplinary boundaries, with complex research problems requiring the integration of new knowledge across a range of disciplines. This calls for researchers with interdisciplinary training, as in bioinformatics with its requirements for mathematics, computer science, and biology. Existing institutional boundaries, such as academic departments in universities, however, often have the effect of rewarding study and research that is focused on more traditional disciplines.[4]

Partnerships between universities and firms that cut across disciplines, though often challenging to implement and manage, are increasingly important to progress in such areas as biotechnology and information technologies as they become more interdependent. While projects led by individual investigators remain vital to general scientific and engineering advancement, solving complex problems in new areas such as bioinformatics and next-generation computing requires larger, multidisciplinary collaborations among scientists and engineering researchers.[5] Partnerships involving universities, government agencies

---

[2] *Ibid.*

[3] See Roger Noll, "Federal R&D in the Anti-Terrorist Era," in *Innovation Policy and the Economy, Vol. 3*, Adam B. Jaffe, Joshua Lerner and Scott Stern, eds., Cambridge, MA: MIT Press, 2002.

[4] See Paula E. Stephan and Grant Black, "Bioinformatics: Emerging Opportunities and Emerging Gaps," National Research Council, *Capitalizing on New Needs and New Opportunities, op. cit.*, 2002.

[5] Bioinformatics is a key example of a highly multidisciplinary field requiring workers with interdisciplinary training. See Paula E. Stephan and Grant Black, "Bioinformatics: Emerging Opportunities and Emerging Gaps" in this volume. The authors find that the field of bioinformatics is highly multidisciplinary, requiring a combination of understanding and skills in mathematics, computer science, and biology. Their paper explores constraints to more robust multidisciplinary research in this important area.

and industry groups can help foster such collaboration by funding multidisciplinary research projects focused on complex problems.[6]

- **Linking Innovation at the Federal, State, and Local Levels**

Partnering between the public and private sectors takes places in multiple arenas. State and local governments often actively promote domestic industries, particularly as they compete in the global marketplace (see Box E). Some states have gone further to develop programs to foster the growth of innovative high-technology firms and the clusters of expertise and research that nurture them.[7] In addition, angel and venture capital investing does not follow political boundaries, but is regionally based, constrained by the mobility of investors (often one day's travel for angels) and the availability of investment opportunities.

In the U.S. federal system of government, political decision making occurs in multiple and often overlapping jurisdictions.[8] This polycentric decision making presents special challenges in integrating R&D activity, especially when it is conducted at different physical locations, often in separate legal jurisdictions. Partnerships can help link activities, for example, in a national laboratory with complementary efforts underway at a state university, and small companies in a local technology cluster. Appropriately structured partnerships among industry, universities, and gov-

---

[6]Federal laboratories offer important capabilities and lessons from experience in dealing with complex research problems. Historically, NIH has not directly supported industry R&D, but this is changing. In 1998, NIH laboratories entered into 166 CRADAs, and in 1999 NIH's Small Business Innovation Research Program awarded more than $300 million to small companies. See Leon Rosenberg, "Partnerships in the Biotechnology Enterprise" in National Research Council, *Capitalizing on New Needs and New Opportunities: Government-Industry Partnerships in Biotechnology and Information Technologies, op cit.*, pp. 111-115, discusses the extent and importance of university-industry partnerships in the biomedical field. For an account of the increasing relationships between non-profit research institutions and for-profit firms, see Chris Adams, "Laboratory Hybrids: How Adroit Scientists Aid Biotech Companies with Taxpayer Money—NIH Grants Go to Non-profits Tied to For-profit Firms Set up by Researchers," *Wall Street Journal,* New York: Dow Jones and Company, January 30, 2001.

[7]One example is the California Council on Science and Technology (CCST), which is the leading partnership of industry, academia, and government in that state. Its mission is to identify ways that science and technology can be used to improve California's economy and quality of life. As a nonpartisan, impartial, and not-for-profit corporation, it is designed to offer expert advice to the state and to provide solutions to science and technology policy issues. For more information, see <http://www.ccst.ucr.edu/>.

[8]Michael Polanyi coined the term "polycentricity." See Polanyi, *Logic of Liberty*, Chicago: University of Chicago Press, 1951, pp. 170-84. For a classic description of polycentric governance in the United States, see Alexis de Tocqueville, *Democracy in America,* Chicago: University of Chicago Press, 2000. For a modern analysis, see Vincent Ostrom, *The Meaning of American Federalism: Constituting a Self-Governing Society*, San Francisco: Institute for Contemporary Studies Press, 1991. The notion of polycentric governance stands in contrast to decentralized governance, which often implies a devolution or delegation of authority from a center of power.

ernmental organizations at the federal, state, and local levels can join together disparate elements within a *de facto* system of innovation. Such an approach can combine under appropriate conditions the advantages of localized innovation with the benefits of national integration.

Toward More Effective Partnerships

The need to advance new technologies, often in support of national missions, and often involving national laboratories, universities, and large and small firms

Box E. Developing Links Among Federal Agencies—The Case of TRP

In addition to fostering links among centers of innovation at the federal, state, and local levels, some partnerships help foster greater coordination among government agencies. Whatever its other merits, the Technology Reinvestment Project (TRP) is reported as having a positive impact on interagency cooperation.

As one TRP participant recollects, "following several weeks of intense joint program review with counterparts from five other agencies during the TRP, technology program managers grew to respect the competence and quality of the people and programs in these other agencies (whom, surprisingly, they had often never before met). Interaction among these individuals increased dramatically after that. Indeed, a hidden but direct result of the TRP was that these functions of the government became more effective overall. For example, rather than creating a new program with sub-critical funding in each new "hot" technical area as they had always done in the past, program managers would consult their counterparts in other agencies, and at least informally coordinate the design, management and execution of these new programs. It became conceivable that a new technology area might achieve a critical mass of funding through a well-coordinated set of complementary efforts in the S&T agencies, rather than have funding in the area be dissipated (as usual) among a large number of competing programs where overlaps and gaps dominate the research landscape."

Interagency partnerships for initiatives in the style of the TRP are an excellent way to improve the effectiveness of federal innovation programs. While, formal agency program coordination may still be necessary, such as through the White House Office of Science and Technology Policy, promoting productive informal relationships is also a "best practice."

has generated a remarkably wide range of public-private partnerships. An illustrative list here would include partnerships in such sectors as electronic storage, flat-panel displays, turbine technologies, new textile manufacturing techniques, new materials, magnetic storage, next-generation vehicles, batteries, biotechnology, optoelectronics, and ship construction.[9] The list would also include federal programs such as the National Manufacturing Initiative, National Science Foundation's (NSF) engineering research centers, NSF's science and technology centers, the National Institute of Standards and Technology's Manufacturing Extension and Advanced Technology Program, and the multi-agency Small Business Innovation Research program, among others.

University-industry cooperation is also on the upswing, with a significant percentage of university R&D now provided by industry[10] and through innovative cooperation efforts, such as the MARCO program. In addition, there are a large number of cooperative research and development agreements between private firms and national laboratories. Some of these, such as the EUVL CRADA, involving companies, laboratories, and universities, are making significant technological contributions.

Despite the political disputes that sometimes surround partnerships, a *de facto* consensus emerged in the late 1980s concerning the utility of public-private partnerships. As Coburn and Berglund noted in the mid-1990s, "The federal government has undergone a sea change the past few years in its approach to the private sector. The broad awareness of and support for these activities in Congress and their spread throughout the $80 billion federal R&D system ensure that they will continue into the next Administration and beyond. *The debate should address not whether these programs will endure, but whether they are shaped properly—at the program and aggregate levels—to achieve the desired benefits.*" [11]

Indeed, the proliferation of partnership programs, and the diversity of their structures and goals, underscores the need for a better understanding of cooperation among public and private sectors to conduct research and bring new technologies to commercial application. Contributing to this new focus on public-private partnership, the Committee has focused its study on three major elements of partnership activity: These are science and technology parks and regional growth clusters, industry consortia, and government awards to fund innovation. The Committee's analysis of each is summarized below.

---

[9]As noted, the Department of Energy also had 700 CRADAs in operation in 1999 to carry out collaborations in research and development.

[10]Industry support of university research has grown from $1.45 billion in 1994 to $2.16 billion in 1999, an annual increase of nearly 10 percent. See Charles F. Larson, "The Boom in Industry Research," *Issues in Science and Technology,* Summer 2000.

[11]See Coburn and Berglund, op. cit. (emphasis added).

SCIENCE AND TECHNOLOGY PARKS AND REGIONAL GROWTH CLUSTERS

Promoting innovation-led growth by encouraging knowledge clusters through the development of science and technology (S&T) parks around the nucleus of national laboratories and research facilities is a key element of public-private partnerships in the United States and a critical factor in the realignment of the missions of U.S. research facilities in the post-Cold War environment.

The fact that firms group together to profit from shared expertise and services has encouraged interest in fostering industry clusters to enhance regional development.[12] In this regard Paul Krugman has reintroduced Alfred Marshall's three-fold classification of externalities "as arising from the ability of producers to share specialized providers of inputs; the advantages to both employers and workers of a thick labor market; and localized spillovers of knowledge, especially through personal interaction."[13] AnnaLee Saxenian has pointed out, in addition, that geographic proximity can foster, through repeated interaction, the mutual trust needed to sustain cooperation and to speed continual recombination of knowledge and skill. The importance of this activity leads Saxenian to observe that "paradoxically, regions offer an important source of competitive advantage even as production and markets become increasingly global." [14]

Historically such clusters often develop around a federally funded nucleus; one example is the high-technology industries that emerged and grew around the government laboratories and major universities in the Boston area. In other cases (e.g., Silicon Valley) multiple private industries interacting with a major university, and irrigated with substantial and sustained federal funding, created powerful developmental synergies.[15]

The success of S&T parks is derived from a variety of factors.[16] These include the presence and involvement of a large research university, existence of a

---

[12]Michael I. Luger and Harvey A. Goldstein (Technology in the Garden; Research Parks & Regional Economic Development, Chapel Hill: University of North Carolina Press, 1991, p. 34) write, "One of the conceptual difficulties is that there is no consensus about the definition of success. . . . The most commonly cited goals relate to economic development. But both the literature and our data from interviews with park developers, elected officials, university administrators, business leaders, and others confirm the existence of other goals, including technology transfer, land development, and enhancement of the research opportunities and capacities of affiliated universities."

[13]See Paul Krugman, "Some Chaotic Thoughts on Regional Dynamics," at <http://www.wws.princeton.edu/~pkrugman/temin.html>.

[14]See AnnaLee Saxenian, *Regional Advantage, op. cit.*, p. 161.

[15]See Martin Kenney, ed., *Understanding Silicon Valley, The Anatomy of an Entrepreneurial Region,* Stanford: Stanford University Press, 2000.

[16]See David B. Audretsch, "The Prospects for a Technology Park at Ames: A New Economy Model for Industry-Government Partnership?" in National Research Council, A Review of the New Initiatives at the NASA Ames Research Center, C. Wessner, ed., Washington, D.C.: National Academy Press, 2001, p. 119.

critical mass of knowledge workers, availability of funding over sustained periods, commitment of leadership to facilitate and guide the park's development, the availability of physical infrastructure and quality-of-life amenities, and importantly the presence and willingness of individuals and teams in the private sector to commercialize some of the knowledge generated.[17] If the benefits of parks are to be realized, a critical combination of these factors has to be present.

The goals of S&T parks and the definition of success vary a great deal. Traditional S&T parks are expected to diffuse knowledge and technology and thus provide an engine for regional growth. In practice, S&T parks often combine multiple goals. The S&T Park adjacent to Sandia National Laboratories in Albuquerque, New Mexico, for example, is designed to encourage close cooperation between Sandia and the private sector on common technological challenges, while sharing costs and expertise. This cooperation is also expected to contribute to a regional environment conducive to science-based economic growth. However, the goals of S&T parks can vary substantially. NASA's Ames Research Center is a case in point. Located in the heart of Silicon Valley, Ames seeks to enable NASA to achieve its mission by providing economical access to technological capabilities *external* to NASA. The park's goal is to draw in tacit knowledge from the exceptional technological and entrepreneurial community around Ames, while serving both as a source of trained personnel and as a conduit for laboratory innovations.[18] The Committee's analysis of the Sandia and Ames S&T parks is summarized below.

The Sandia S&T Park

National laboratories, as repositories of knowledge and scientific aptitude, represent important sources of development as nuclei for growth clusters. The federal government has made and continues to make substantial investments in the laboratories, which have developed a significant store of technology and talent. In their role as a steward of the nation's nuclear weapons programs, the Sandia National Laboratories currently expend approximately $1.3 billion annually and employ over 7,000 people—many of whom are highly trained. Labora-

[17]As Luger and Goldstein note, "The overall policy lesson we have drawn from this analysis is that in many regions research parks by themselves will not be a wise investment. The success rate among all announced parks is relatively low. ... Research parks will be most successful in helping to stimulate economic development in regions that already are richly endowed with resources that attract highly educated scientists and engineers." See Michael Luger and Harvey Goldstein, Technology in the Garden, Research Parks and Regional Economic Development, Chapel Hill: University of North Carolina Press, 1991, p. 184.

[18]See National Research Council, *A Review of the New Initiatives at the NASA Ames Research Center, op. cit.*

tories such as Sandia possess unique capabilities, facilities, and equipment (such as the teraflop computer), thus constituting a valuable national resource.

Just as the laboratories potentially offer much to the private sector, the laboratories themselves recognize that they cannot fulfill their mission in isolation, especially given today's rapid pace of innovation. To remain effective, laboratories such as Sandia and others understand that they must stay abreast of the rapid technological change taking place in the commercial arena. This means building and maintaining ties to the private sector. One means of encouraging this mutually beneficial exchange is the Sandia Science and Technology (S&T) Park, which is contiguous to the laboratory in Albuquerque.[19]

The Sandia S&T Park is an entity legally separate from the laboratory itself. It is perhaps best viewed as a mechanism, in conjunction with companies engaged in cooperative research and development agreements (CRADAs) with Sandia, to help the laboratory fulfill its mission while also drawing on the unique assets of the Albuquerque region. An undertaking of this scope is inherently complex and in the case of this national laboratory there were a number of significant policy issues to be addressed.[20] The interest of the Sandia managers in addressing these issues early in the process is reflected in the substantial progress the initiative has achieved thus far.[21]

The Ames S&T Park

NASA is also seeking to capitalize on its existing assets and promising new technological trends in biotechnology, nanotechnology, and information technology. NASA's Ames Research Center, at Moffett Field, California, has developed a strategic approach to the use of its extensive human and physical resources consistent with NASA's overall mission in order to leverage its own particular research capabilities and exceptional location in the heart of Silicon Valley.[22]

---

[19]National Research Council, *Industry-Laboratory Partnerships: A Review of the Sandia Science and Technology Park Initiative,* C. Wessner, ed., Washington, D.C.: National Academy Press, 1999.

[20]David Mowery, "Collaborative R&D: How Effective Is It," *Issues in Science and Technology,* Fall 1998, p. 40. For a comprehensive view of the "alternative futures," for the Department of Energy National Laboratories, see the "Galvin Report," *Alternative Futures for the Department of Energy National Laboratories,* Washington, D.C.: U.S. Department of Energy, 1995.

[21]Since its official groundbreaking in May 1998, the park has attracted 10 companies and 590 employees. It has developed 219,288 square feet of occupied space and has attracted $16,565,684 in funds-in and in-kind dollars to Sandia labs from tenants in the park through CRADAs and licensing agreements. In addition, it has fostered $12,703,951 in contracts from Sandia labs to tenants in the park and $540,000 in contracts between tenants in the park. Total investment in the park is $61,785,028 ($48,556,188 in private funds + $13,228,840 in public funds).

[22]See presentations by Sam Venneri and William Berry in National Research Council, *A Review of the New Initiatives at the NASA Ames Research Center, op. cit.*

The Ames Research Center has embarked on a program to develop a science and technology park to bring together leading high-technology companies and exceptional universities, such as Carnegie Mellon University and the University of California at Santa Cruz, to contribute to its unique mission and to the educational and research requirements of the region. The park includes shared research facilities and public-private cooperation in teaching and training, and its goal is to contribute to NASA's core missions of research, exploration, and discovery.[23] The park is also intended to facilitate NASA's commercialization of technologies developed by agency scientists and engineers and to contribute to related national benefits such as higher computer dependability.[24]

Both the Sandia and Ames initiatives highlight the potential to be gained from effective, regionally based partnerships. The analysis set out in the next major section emphasizes that gains from cooperative research activity can best be achieved when these undertakings have clear goals, develop metrics for measuring achievement, and conduct frequent assessments.

CONSORTIA

The Nature of Consortia

An industry consortium as a framework for precompetitive cooperative research can help individual firms or research groups develop new technologies. It can help a firm overcome market situations where the nature of the good inhibits it from taking up, at its own expense, the risk of developing new technologies.[25] Consortia are heterogeneous in scope, organization, and purpose. The fact that there is no set model of how a consortium is supposed to be structured can be considered an advantage in that a consortium can be tailored to account for the particular nature of good in question and the specific perceived market opportunities that present themselves. Recognizing this, the Committee's study of public-private partnerships has focused on the case of SEMATECH not as a model to be

[23]Given the scope and ambition of these objectives, the then NASA Administrator, Daniel Goldin, asked the NRC's Board on Science, Technology, and Economic Policy to review the Ames initiatives. See National Research Council, A Review of the New Initiatives at the NASA Ames Research Center, op. cit.

[24]Other initiatives under consideration include the integration of SBIR grants with a planned onsite incubator, virtual or distance collaboration, and possibly a new public venture capital program.

[25]Link, *op. cit.* suggests that public-private partnerships represent a key instrument to overcome disincentives to socially beneficial R&D activity.

blindly copied but as an example from which to draw positive framework principles of broad relevance.[26]

Consortia can help reduce research costs and help accelerate high-spillover technologies by coordinating precompetitive work among firms. Activities, such as those related to developing platform technologies and common standards, can be organized cooperatively, even as firms compete privately in their separate R&D efforts.[27] In an R&D consortium a certain portion and type of the R&D—often involving research upstream from the market —is funneled into the organization where it is carried out collectively and is deployed by a variety of other firms.[28] Firms also continue to compete privately through carrying on their own application-related R&D programs. Thus, firms cooperate when it is in their individual and collective interest to cooperate and compete when it is in their individual interest and the interests of consumers to compete. In his analysis of the SEMATECH consortium, Kenneth Flamm posits three related motives for firms to engage in such consortia-based cooperation.[29]

- *Sharing Information:* The first is to share information among firms so that each firm can achieve a certain level of technological progress at a lower cost and more rapidly than any single firm could achieve on its own.
- *Internalizing High-Spillover Projects*: The second is to conduct research where the high-spillover nature of the product inhibits individual firms from proceeding independently.

---

[26]As one of the earliest public-private partnerships, SEMATECH, the semiconductor consortium, has often been cited as a example for other consortia. To be sure, some specifics relating to SEMATECH differ from the realities faced by firms in other industries. One instance encountered in the Committee's study of public-private partnerships is that firms in the semiconductor industry appear to have had the advantage of a much clearer research path than that being confronted by the solid-state lighting industry today. See National Research Council, Partnerships in Solid-State Lighting, op cit.

[27]See Peter Grindley, David C Mowery, and Brian Silverman, "SEMATECH and Collaborative Research: Lessons in the Design of High-Technology Consortia," *Journal of Policy Analysis and Management* 13(4), Fall 1994, pp. 723-758.

[28]Consortia, a hybrid form of industrial organization, are distinct from cartels or competitive joint ventures. In an R&D cartel firms jointly commit to individual investments in R&D activities, with agreement on how much each will invest in R&D. Here each knows that some of the results of their individual R&D are going to spill over to the other firms. In a competitive R&D joint venture each company agrees to funnel its R&D through a single organization without committing to a level of spending. Both these organizational forms are prone to suffer from the free-rider problem—wherein each firm would attempt to contribute less to the joint effort in the hopes of taking advantage of full cooperation from others. If most or all firms follow the same strategy, the optimum amount of innovation is not achieved. See Kenneth Flamm, "SEMATECH Revisited: Assessing Consortium Impacts on Semiconductor Industry R&D," in National Research Council, *Securing the Future: Regional and National Programs to Support the Semiconductor Industry, op. cit.*

[29]*Ibid.*

- *Increasing Spillovers*: The third is to create incentives that encourage knowledge transfers (or spillovers) and thus, in a "virtuous circle," increase the overall level of innovation activity in the industry.

Partnership roles for government in the case of consortia include legally enabling such cooperation, contributing to the funding of research activities, supporting research cooperation with national laboratories, and through grants or facilities to encourage advanced research on shared platform technologies.[30] The reasons for government participation vary; they can invoke broad goals such as national security or the international competitiveness of a domestic industry or in developing technologies that offer substantial environmental benefits.

Well structured, well managed consortia offer a variety of advantages. Consortia can help:

- Establish research goals and directions that expedite commercialization of technology and support for government missions.
- Coordinate basic and underlying research with development of infrastructure, process, and design technology.
- Preserve commercial incentives, including exclusive rights to certain intellectual property for product design.
- Facilitate development of comprehensive technology roadmaps that illuminate critical challenges, gaps, and timetables.
- Aid in the wide dissemination of general research information, including roadmaps.
- Enable broad licensing of certain intellectual property related to product manufacturing, contributing to de facto industry standards.
- Create a means of sharing certain non-competitive research costs and risks.

[30]The widespread perception in the 1980s that U.S. technological leadership was slipping led policymakers to conclude that existing U.S. antitrust laws and penalties were too restrictive and were possibly impeding the ability of U.S. companies to compete in global markets. The passage of the National Cooperative Research Act (NCRA) in 1984 encouraged U.S. firms to collaborate on generic, pre-competitive research. To gain protection from antitrust litigation, NCRA required firms engaging in research joint ventures to register them with the U.S. Department of Justice. By the end of 1996, more than 665 research joint ventures had been registered. In 1993, Congress again relaxed restrictions—this time on cooperative production activities—by passing the National Cooperative Research and Production Act, which enables participants to work together to apply technologies developed by their research joint ventures. SEMATECH has perhaps been the most significant private R&D consortium formed since the U.S. Congress passed the National Cooperative Research Act of 1984. See A. L. Link, "Research Joint Ventures: Patterns From Federal Register Filings." Review of Industrial Organization 11, No. 5 (October): 617-28, 1996; Kenneth Flamm, "SEMATECH Revisited" op cit., p. 1; and N.S. Vonortas, *Cooperation in Research and Development*, Norwell, MA: Lower Academic Publishers, 1997. See also, National Science Board, Science and Engineering Indicators, 1998, Arlington, VA: National Science Foundation, 1998.

The Case of SEMATECH

As noted in Chapter IV, SEMATECH was founded in 1987 amidst what was seen as a crisis in the U.S. semiconductor industry. The market share of the U.S. industry was steadily declining, with the Japanese industry showing corresponding increases as Figure 4 shows.[31] In addition to the impact of the trade practices noted above, there were also problems with manufacturing quality for U.S. producers. For example, in some cases productivity of Japanese semiconductor firms had surpassed, even with the same technology, those of their American counterparts.[32] To meet this challenge 14 U.S. semiconductor manufacturers, with the support of the U.S. government, joined to form the SEMATECH consortium.[33] This required a change in the mindset of industry leaders, who as fierce competitors were hesitant to cooperate with each other and, as independent entrepreneurs, uncertain about cooperating with the government. The government, or at least parts of it, was hesitant as well. After having played a major role in the industry's origin, largely through procurement contracts, the U.S. government's involvement with the industry was primarily that of a customer, and even that role was much diminished from that of the 1960s and 1970s.

The consortium represents a leading example of public-private experimentation in cooperative R&D. As Kenneth Flamm notes, "in terms of size, visibility, and public policy impact, SEMATECH has perhaps been the most significant private R&D consortium formed in almost two decades that have passed since the passage by the U.S. Congress of the National Cooperative Research Act of 1984, which granted partial antitrust exemption to registered U.S. R&D consortia."[34]

At the time of SEMATECH's founding, industry leaders became concerned that they needed to improve manufacturing quality and resolved to find a way to improve the situation collectively.[35] Despite the independence and fierce competitiveness among firms in the industry, the Semiconductor Industry Association took the unusual step of approaching the government and making the argument that collective action was necessary for the sake of long-term U.S. economic

[31] *Ibid.*

[32] See Jeffrey T. Macher, David C. Mowery, and David A. Hodges, "Semiconductors," in *U.S. Industry in 2000: Studies in Competitive Performance, op.cit.*

[33] For a first-hand account of the SEMATECH experiment, see the statement of Gordon Moore in National Research Council, *Securing the Future: Regional and National Programs to Support the Semiconductor Industry, op. cit.*

[34] Kenneth Flamm, "SEMATECH Revisited," *op. cit.*, p. 1.

[35] See Gordon Moore's presentation in the Proceedings section of the Committee's report on the semiconductor industry. National Research Council, *Securing the Future: Regional and National Programs to Support the Semiconductor Industry, op. cit.*

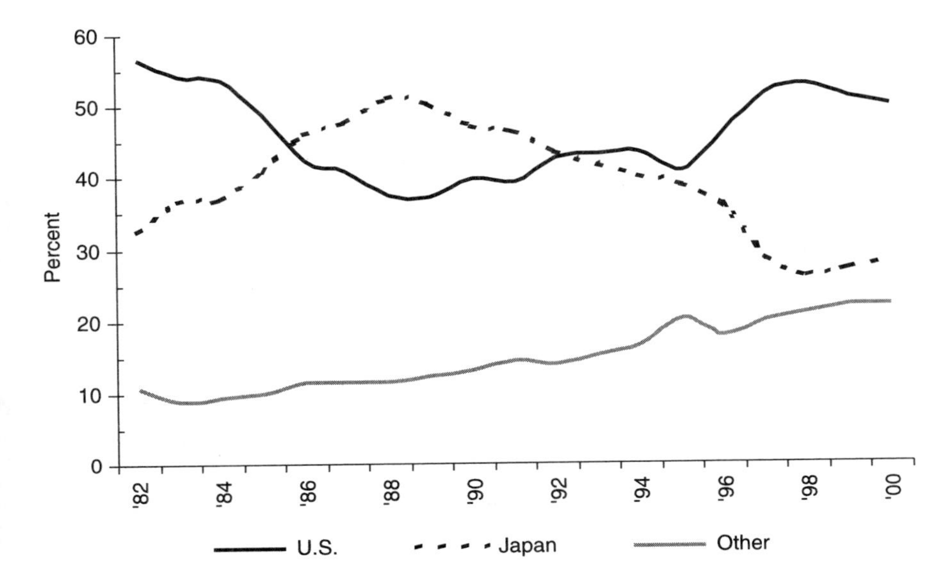

FIGURE 4 Worldwide semiconductor market share.
SOURCE: SIA.

competitiveness and the national defense.[36] After much debate the industry and the Reagan Administration agreed on a unique arrangement in which the government and participating companies jointly funded the consortium, with the companies investing $100 million and the federal government matching that amount on an annual basis.[37] From 1987 to 1996, the government investment in SEMATECH totaled about $850 million.[38] Participating companies included most of the largest semiconductor companies in the U.S., and all 14 companies appointed rep-

[36]The move to form SEMATECH occurred only when the top executives from the best U.S. electronics companies came to the sobering realization that they could not prevail alone. As Hedrick Smith, a well-known commentator, noted in *Rethinking America,* (New York: Random House, 1995, p. 385) "the mere formation of SEMATECH required a radically new mindset at some of America's leading high-tech corporations."

[37]Membership dues were fixed at 1 percent of semiconductor sales, with a minimum contribution of $1 million and a maximum of $15 million.

[38]See the presentation by Gordon Moore in *Securing the Future: Regional and National Programs to Support the Semiconductor Industry, op. cit.* Moore points out that the government return on this investment has been substantial in that Intel alone pays in taxes, each quarter, several times the amount of the earlier federal contribution.

resentatives to work closely with the consortium.[39] This close and effective cooperation with its membership was one of the distinguishing features of its operation.[40]

Initially planned to last five years, SEMATECH's accomplishments and the continued challenges facing the industry led to its extension for an additional five years. Before the second term expired, the commercial success of participating firms led the SEMATECH Board to decide that it was not necessary to continue government support. As one participant noted, this decision came "much to the surprise of the people back here in Washington, where programs seem to have a life of their own."[41] Importantly, the end of the government's contribution to the consortium's operations did not signal the end of the program. On the contrary, after a period of adjustment, industry support again expanded.[42]

Today there is a widespread perception in industry and among informed academics that SEMATECH played a significant role in the resurgence of the U.S. semiconductor industry, albeit one that is probably not possible to quantify.[43] As noted in Part IV, this view of SEMATECH's contribution is widely shared outside the United States, not least in Japan and Europe, where major cooperative efforts influenced by the SEMATECH experience are underway.[44]

---

[39]The Semiconductor Industry Association put forward a proposal in May 1987 for a research consortium supported by shared government-industry funding. The original members were IBM, Intel, Motorola, Texas Instruments, National Semiconductor, Advanced Micro Devices, Lucent Technologies, Compaq Computer Corp., Hewlett-Packard Technology, Conexant Systems, NCR Microelectronics, Harris Semiconductor, LSI Logic, and Micron Technology. With the last three in the list dropping out in the early 1990s, 11 of the original 14 members of SEMATECH remain today. For an early review of the SEMATECH R&D program, see the GAO study, SEMATECH's Technological Progress and Proposed R&D Program, GAO/RCEED/92-223 BR, Washington, D.C., July 1992.

[40]L.D. Browning, J.M. Beyer, and J.C. Shetler, "Building Cooperation in a Competitive Industry: SEMATECH and the Semiconductor Industry," *Academy of Management Journal*, 38(1) 1995, pp. 113-115. For a comparison of the operations and successes of SEMATECH and Microelectronics and Computer Technology Corporation, see Horrigan, *op. cit.*

[41]See comments by Gordon Moore in the Proceedings of National Research Council, *Securing the Future: Regional and National Programs to Support the Semiconductor Industry, op cit.*

[42]In July 1994, the SEMATECH board voted to terminate government support for its effort, with fiscal year 1996 slated to be the final year of government funding. Despite the end to government funding SEMATECH members have agreed to continue this innovative program, with core funding provided exclusively by corporate contributions.

[43]For an overview of SEMATECH, see National Research Council, *Conflict and Cooperation, op. cit.* pp. 148-151. For an analysis of the empirical evidence, see Kenneth Flamm, "SEMATECH Revisited: Assessing Consortium Impacts on Semiconductor Industry R&D," in National Research Council, *National and Regional Programs to Support the Semiconductor Industry, op. cit.* See also, Peter Grindley, David C. Mowery and Brian Silverman. "SEMATECH and Collaborative Research: Lessons in the Design of High Technology Consortia," *Journal of Policy Analysis and Management*, 13(4) 1994, pp. 723-758.

[44]For a review of efforts in Japan, Europe, and elsewhere in this regard, see Thomas Howell, "Competing Programs, Government Support for Microelectronics," in National Research Council, *Securing the Future: Regional and National Programs to Support the Semiconductor Industry, op. cit.*

(1995).

Perhaps the most appropriate measure of SEMATECH's contribution is the reaction of the market itself—that is, the willingness of industry participants to continue to provide matching funds over a sustained period; and then independently for these same firms to continue and expand the consortium with private resources and new members. In short, the apparent emulation by other nations, the continued participation and funding by private firms, and the sustained technical inputs of SEMATECH, all give credence to claims of positive contributions for the consortium.[45]

SEMATECH's Contributions to Best Practice

- **A Cooperative Approach to Quality**

SEMATECH's purpose was to revive a seriously weakened U.S. industry through collaborative research and pooling of manufacturing knowledge.[46] A central element of the challenges facing the U.S. semiconductor industry was manufacturing quality. U.S. manufacturing standards had fallen behind the standards of the Japanese semiconductor producers. The problem was manifested in lower manufacturing yields, higher costs, and inferior product quality.[47] For example, users of U.S. and Japanese devices discovered that Japanese memory products had defect rates that were one-half to one-third those of comparable U.S. memory products. Similarly, skills in managing the development and introduction of new process technologies enabled Japanese semiconductor manufacturers to ramp up new products more rapidly than their U.S. counterparts.[48]

By the mid-1980s, the leading U.S. semiconductor firms had recognized the strategic importance of quality and began to initiate quality improvement pro-

[45]Empirical analysis of SEMATECH's success is limited. Some of what exists is flawed in terms of the assumptions underlying its econometrics. For a review of the literature and an updated assessment, see Kenneth Flamm, "SEMATECH Revisited: Assessing Consortium Impacts on Semiconductor Industry R&D," *op. cit.*

[46]Semiconductor manufacturers—secretive, often adversarial competitors—faced an early critical challenge to effective cooperation within SEMATECH in the fear that cooperation would reveal proprietary secrets to competitors. As Larry Browning and Judy Shetler note in their comprehensive study of the consortium, this initial reluctance centered around three questions: "What technology could they use for the mission of improving performance?" "What firm would they want to contribute a cutting-edge proprietary process?" and "What would be the use in working on anything else?" See Larry D. Browning and Judy C. Shetler, *SEMATECH: Saving the U.S. Semiconductor Industry,* College Station: Texas A&M University Press, 2000, p. 22.

[47]See National Research Council, *Conflict and Cooperation in National Competition for High-Technology Industry, op. cit.*, p. 142.

[48]See Jeffrey T. Macher, David C. Mowery, and David A. Hodges, "Semiconductors," *op. cit.*, pp. 255-256.

grams. A key element in this effort was the formation of the SEMATECH consortium (See Box F), which in part reflected the belief that the Japanese cooperative programs had been instrumental in the success of Japanese producers.[49]

- **Industry Leadership**

After an early focus on developing a manufacturing facility to help solve manufacturing problems (rather than rely on a lab), the consortium eventually focused on three goals that involved improving:

- Manufacturing processes;
- Factory management;
- Industry infrastructure, especially the supply base of equipment and materials.[50]

Keeping the consortium's activities relevant to the interests of member companies and effective in meeting their needs was a central focus of the consortium's management. To do so, the consortium relied on the direct involvement of its member companies' leadership and on quality research staff (called assignees) rotated from its member companies.[51] Senior executives of member companies participated actively on the consortium's Board of Directors. An executive technical advisory board set priorities for research, development, and testing activities within the consortium. A series of subgroups, called technical advisory groups, approved and advised on specific projects.[52] This close involvement substantially facilitated the exchange of information among members and ensured the continued relevance and application of the consortium's research.

- **Cooperation Between Equipment Suppliers and Device Makers**

The consortium also encouraged cooperation between U.S. semiconductor equipment suppliers and the device producers. Cooperation between suppliers and device makers was facilitated by collaboration with the Semiconductor Equip-

---

[49]See Larry D. Browning and Judy C. Shetler, *SEMATECH, Saving the U.S. Semiconductor Industry, op. cit.*, Chapter 1.

[50]See Larry D. Browning and Judy C. Shetler, *SEMATECH, Saving the U.S. Semiconductor Industry, op. cit.*, p. 205.

[51]This was important in that it helped keep SEMATECH research tied closely to the changing interests of its members and helped facilitate the transmission and adoption of its contributions. MCC's more arm's length relationship did not work as well. See John Horrigan, "Cooperating Competitors: A Comparison of MCC and SEMATECH," *op. cit.*

[52]Browning and Shelter, *op. cit.*, p. 207.

ment and Materials Institute (SEMI), which provided institutional support and a voice for the equipment and materials suppliers to the industry.[53]

Cooperation between the device makers and the equipment suppliers, while sometimes difficult, became an important focus for the consortium.[54] At the time, many of the equipment companies were one-product firms formed to build a particular kind of machine with the company's fortunes tied to the life cycle of that equipment. SEMATECH worked with these companies to develop reliable tools, to focus on total quality control, and to understand the needs of the industry and the increasing sophistication of the manufacturing process. SEMATECH's members began to recognize that much of the important work required to improve manufacturing equipment did not have to be done by each company individually, but could be done by the consortium centrally.[55]

- **The Roadmap**

> *"I guess part of why a roadmap makes sense to us is that with complex technology there's no one right way to go."*
>
> Bill Spencer, Chairman Emeritus, SEMATECH

The need for coordination among SEMATECH's members was realized when it came time to identify those science and technology applications that had high potential promise and how then to accelerate the technology transfer to useful applications. This led to the development of the first technology roadmap. A roadmap is in essence a graphical portrayal of the relationships among science, technology, and applications over a period. Its scope includes technology management and planning; strategies for enhancing communications among researchers, technologists, product managers, suppliers, users, and other stakeholders, in-

[53]See Peter Grindley, David C. Mowery, and Brian Silverman, "SEMATECH and Collaborative Research: Lessons in the Design of High-Technology Consortia," *op. cit.*

[54]Kalman Kaufman, then of Applied Materials, noted the guidance from the Roadmap (see next section) was not always accurate and, in the case of the conversion to 300mm wafers, caused significant loss to some suppliers. See the comments by Kalman Kaufman of Applied Materials in the proceedings of National Research Council, *Securing the Future: Regional and National Programs to Support the Semiconductor Industry, op. cit.*

[55]See the presentation by Gordon Moore in National Research Council, *Securing the Future: Regional and National Programs to Support the Semiconductor Industry, op. cit.* The consortium also developed a cost-of-ownership model for manufacturing tools that described problems in detail.

cluding technology and product marketing; identifying gaps in R&D programs; and identifying obstacles to rapid and low-cost product development.[56]

Created in 1992, the first roadmap was developed in response to a request for information by the government about the most pressing research and development needs of the industry. Subsequent roadmaps were developed in 1994 and 1997. With the internationalization of SEMATECH, the International Technology Roadmap for Semiconductors (IRTS) was formed in 1998, with a schedule of regular reports and updates.

The development of technology roadmaps was a cooperative effort with SEMATECH, the SIA, and the SRC pioneering the creation of an innovative management decision aid that improves the coordination of consortium-based research activities and resources in an increasingly complex and uncertain technological environment. The widespread adoption of the roadmap concept by other industries (e.g., optoelectronics and nanotechnologies) underscores the value of this collaborative multi-institutional approach.[57]

Addressing New Challenges

Noting that SEMATECH provides evidence of "a government-industry partnership that can contribute," some participants emphasize that the challenge for prospective consortia is to identify a charge clearly at the outset. Without a very specific charter, a multi-corporation organization may not have any more impact than a single laboratory. The impact can be greatest when the problems exceed what a single company can do—a case in point would be the challenges of a new lithography environment. As the industry moves away from optical lithography it faces billion-dollar R&D programs in order to reach the point where it can start operating alternative lithography systems. Addressing a challenge of this magnitude in an effective and timely manner requires some form of industry or industry-government cooperation.[58]

---

[56]See Robert R. Schaller, "Technology Roadmaps: Implications for Innovation, Strategy, and Policy," Ph.D. Dissertation Proposal, Institute for Public Policy, George Mason University, 1999.

[57]The National Nanotechnology Initiative is a case in point. For a recent review, see National Research Council, *Small Wonders, Endless Frontiers: A Review of the National Nanotechnology Initiative*, Washington, D.C.: National Academy Press, 2002.

[58]For more discussion of some of the technical, resource, and organizational challenges facing the semiconductor industry in maintaining the pace predicted by Moore's Law, see National Research Council, *Securing the Future: Regional and National Programs to Support the Semiconductor Industry, op. cit.*

Box F. Lessons from the SEMATECH Consortium

Because of its contributions, SEMATECH is often seen as a model for public-private partnerships.[59] The SEMATECH experience has several lessons for organizing a successful consortium[60]:

Understanding the Need for Cooperation—The range of R&D needs (from basic science to manufacturing infrastructure to whole new industries) is best understood by the industry when working in close cooperation with universities and government research laboratories. To achieve the full benefits of cooperation it is important to

- *Ensure Quality Leadership*, including key leaders of the major participating industries.
- *Convey Your Message* publicly to leaders in the government and private sectors.
- *Focus the Program* on key sectors and build on this developed strength, rather than approach the entire industry.
- *Set Measurable Objectives* for advancing generic or pre-competitive knowledge.
- *Set Uniform Requirements* for participation so that support is not fragmented.
- *Plan First—Spend Later*: Roadmaps are needed before consortia can be properly launched.
- *Develop an Industry-driven Process*. While it continues to benefit from strong leadership, no single entity dominates the consortium or determines its direction. Members reach consensus on technical direction and consortium management implements this direction. Recent cooperative work, such as on extreme ultraviolet lithography, demonstrates that successful consortia are industry driven.

[59]See National Research Council, Supplement B, "Government Support for Technology Development: The SEMATECH Experiment," in *National Competition for High-Technology Industry*, Washington, D.C.: National Academy Press, pp. 141-51.

[60]See remarks by Bill Spencer in the Proceedings section of National Research Council, *Partnerships for Solid-State Lighting, Report on a Workshop, op. cit.*

A Potential Consortium in Solid-State Lighting

The challenges facing the solid-state lighting industry illustrate the role consortia can play in bringing new technology to the marketplace while achieving major national objectives. Solid-state lighting technology has the potential to revolutionize the lighting industry, and—if widely used—reduce energy dependence on overseas oil, enhance environmental quality, and improve productivity.[61]

Because light-emitting diode (LED) and Organic LED (OLED) technologies convert electricity more efficiently into light than today's light bulbs, their widespread use can reduce the nation's consumption of electricity by half, according to estimates highlighted by experts in the Committee's report on *Partnerships for Solid-State Lighting*.[62] Given that 20 percent of all electricity in the United States is used for lighting, the widespread use of solid-state lighting could reduce gross power usage by about 10 percent. Estimates of gross annual savings from this reduction vary from $10 billion in the near future to $70 billion by 2020. This reduced demand for electricity also translates into lower gross emissions from pollutants from power generation.[63] Reduced dependence on scarce energy resources also can contribute to greater U.S. national security.

Additional benefits of solid-state lighting derive from their versatility and wafer-thin size and the fact they do not give off heat. Current fluorescent lighting technologies that illuminate most offices, by comparison, require substantial room—so much so that an average eight-story building, lighted using today's technology, could have an additional floor added through the use of solid-state lighting.

---

[61] For a review of this challenge and opportunities facing this industry, see National Research Council, *Partnerships in Solid-State Lighting, op. cit.*

[62] See remarks by Charles Becker in the Proceedings section of the report, National Research Council, *Partnerships in Solid-State Lighting, op. cit.*

[63] Solid-state lighting, by replacing less efficient lighting devices, is expected to yield significant gross energy savings and environmental benefits. A more complete analysis of the widespread use of solid-state lighting would have to consider the net dynamic impact of this new technology. For instance, under some scenarios innovative applications of the technology might create additional demand for lighting, thus increasing energy use. In principle, to arrive at net benefits one has to account for the externalities that arise with investments in and production of this technology, including opportunity costs of deploying the involved resources in alternative uses. These costs, whether positive or negative, have to be internalized and then subtracted from the gross benefits to arrive at the appropriate net benefit.

> The versatility of OLEDs is generating great enthusiasm among some members of the architectural community. As one expert has remarked, "Imagine a light source so integrated with building materials that with the activation of electric current, simple wood, brick, and concrete surfaces are transformed into a colorful, kinetic, luminous environment—where the infrastructure of the light source is diminished to virtually nothing while the presence of light is magnified."[64]

As analysis of partnerships in solid-state lighting suggests, substantial cooperative, pre-competitive work is required among firms in the lighting industry to overcome remaining technological challenges, and to set standards and common interfaces for solid-state illumination devices. These improvements are needed to enhance mass-market acceptance and promote widespread use of this technology. In turn, such widespread use can help realize the energy savings and environmental benefits that this new technology offers. Knowledge spillovers generated through public-private partnerships in a consortium framework can accelerate this progress by making solid-state lighting more versatile, economical, and therefore acceptable to consumers. A consortium would appear to hold considerable potential to contribute to a range of valuable national goals.

GOVERNMENT AWARDS TO FUND INNOVATION

Firm Size and Sources of Innovation

Small business is widely believed to be a significant source of innovation and employment growth—a perception that has considerable basis in fact.[65] Certainly in the nineteenth century the individual inventor played a central role in U.S. economic development. More recently the role of the small startup firms in regions such as Silicon Valley have reinforced the notion that small business is an important driver of economic growth.

---

[64]Christina Trauthwein, "You Say You Want a Revolution. . ."*Architectural Lighting*, May 2001, p. 43.

[65]A recent report by the Organisation for Economic Cooperation and Development (OECD) notes that small and medium-size enterprises are attracting the attention of policymakers, not least because they are seen as major sources of economic vitality, flexibility, and employment. Small business is especially important as a source of new employment, accounting for a disproportionate share of job creation. See OECD, *Small Business Job Creation and Growth: Facts, Obstacles, and Best Practices*. Paris, 1997. For specifics on job growth, see Steven J. Davis, John Haltiwanger, and Scott Schuh, "Small Business and Job Creation: Dissecting the Myth and Reassessing the Facts," *Business Economics*, 29(3):113-122.

Yet the question of firm size and economic growth has been the subject of debate for much of the twentieth century and beyond. The early part of the twentieth century was marked by the rise of the large-scale enterprise in the United States, and the conventional wisdom held that large firms had compelling advantages in most performance measures—from profitability to productivity. It was widely accepted that large firms could operate at sufficient levels of scale to produce efficiently and generate the resources to develop innovations that would perpetuate market dominance. In 1950 Schumpeter, while pointing to the small entrepreneur as the vanguard of the wave of "creative destruction" that spurred innovation, nonetheless posited that large firms with substantial resources available for R&D would come to dominate capitalist economies.[66] Galbraith later argued that the source of innovation was more plausibly the large firm, which he believed, had the resources available to invest at sufficient scale, not the individual innovator.[67]

Concentration and centralization in research and development, which characterized the early years of the twentieth century, did seem consistent with the ideas about firm size and innovation hypothesized by Schumpeter and Galbraith. The great corporate research laboratories were established at companies such as DuPont, General Electric, and AT&T. In the postwar years RCA's Sarnoff Laboratory was established, and IBM's Yorktown lab and Bell Laboratories enjoyed their heyday, generating innovations in computing and communications that have had profound effects on the U.S. economy and lifestyle.

The Role of Small Firms in Innovation

By the 1970s most data indicate that the story began to change, with small-firm growth accelerating. From 1975 to 1984 employment in firms with between 20 and 99 workers grew by 3.64 percent annually, while employment at firms with more than 1,000 workers grew at only one-third that rate, or 1.25 percent. From 1980 to 1987 the average real GNP per firm decreased by 14 percent, from $245,000 to $200,000.[68] As *The Economist* noted in 1989, large firms are shrink-

---

[66]Joseph Schumpeter, *Capitalism, Socialism and Democracy*. New York: Harper and Row, 1950, p. 110. Many analysts see a split between Schumpeter's early writings, which stress the importance of bold entrepreneurs, and his later writings, where he envisages the demise of bold entrepreneurs and their replacement by a new mode of economic organization. For an analysis of this apparent dichotomy, see Richard N. Langlois, "Schumpeter and the Obsolescence of the Entrepreneur," Working Paper, 91-1503, Department of Economics, University of Connecticut, November 1991.

[67]See John Kenneth Galbraith, *The New Industrial State*. Boston: Houghton Mifflin, 1957. Evidence from the postwar era seemed to support these notions; from 1947 to 1980 the average real gross national product per firm grew from $150,000 to $245,000; see Zoltan J. Acs and David B. Audretsch, *Innovation and Small Firms*. Cambridge, MA: MIT Press, 1991, p 4.

[68]See Acs and Audretsch, *op. cit.*, p. 3.

ing in size and small ones are proliferating; in terms of the source of employment growth, "the trend of a century is being reversed."[69] With respect to large research laboratories, as Rosenbloom and Spencer have noted, a similar reduction in size has occurred, as IBM's Yorktown facility was severely downsized in the 1990s and as the breakup of the Bell System in the 1980s changed the character of Bell Laboratories. Investment in long-term R&D is seen by many as the primary casualty of these changes.[70]

Even before the breakup of the large R&D laboratories there was a growing recognition of the role of small business in furthering technological innovation. The 1980s saw the emergence of such rapidly growing companies as Microsoft and Apple Computing. The 1990s witnessed the rapid growth of the U.S. venture capital industry, which helped high-growth firms to exploit the commercial potential of promising new technologies.[71] To some extent, science and technology policy in the 1980s and 1990s reflected this emphasis on the innovative role of small and rapid-growth business.

Cooperation as a Policy Goal

In the 1970s and 1980s the United States recorded slow economic growth relative to postwar norms, sluggish productivity performance, and a loss of global market share and technological leadership in key U.S. industries, from steel and automobiles to television and semiconductors. There was also considerable concern about a rapidly rising trade deficit.[72] The causes of the sub-par U.S. eco-

---

[69]See "The Rise and Fall of America's Small Firms," *The Economist,* January 21, 1989, pp. 73-74.

[70]See Richard Rosenbloom and William Spencer. *Engines of Innovation: U.S. Industrial Research at the End of an Era.* Boston: Harvard Business Press, 1996. Irwin Lebow supports this view, observing that in the opinion of many, the most significant change brought about by the AT&T divestiture was that Bell Laboratories no longer operates under conditions as favorable to the pursuit of fundamental research, the results of which will not be evident for some time in the future. *Information Highways and Byways: From the Telegraph to the 21st Century*, Piscataway NJ: IEEE Press, 1995, p. 157.

[71]For discussion of the relationship between innovative activity and firm size, see Zoltan J. Acs and David Audretsch, *Innovation and Small Firms*, Cambridge, MA: MIT Press, 1990, chap. 3. They maintain that it is important to recognize that small firms are not necessarily more innovative than large firms are. The relative contribution depends on the sector, market structure, capital intensity, and rate of innovation. Acs and Audretsch emphasize that both large and small firms bring advantages to the innovation process. Large firms have the resources for long-term R&D investments and benefit from substantial advantages, such as economies of scale, investment, and the market power necessary to recoup R&D investments. Small firms tend to have a higher tolerance for risk, are characterized by rapid decision making, and often focus on innovative activity as a core strategy.

[72]For an analysis of the sustainability of the deficit, see Catherine Mann, *Is the U.S. Trade Deficit Sustainable?* Washington, D.C.: Institute for International Economics, 1993. The U.S. Trade Deficit Review Commission was established in October 1998 to review the trade deficit and its implications for the economy as a whole. See <http://www.ustrdc.gov>.

nomic performance defied definitive analysis, but dire warnings of U.S. economic decline and the "deindustrialization" of key manufacturing sectors proliferated.[73]

At the same time, U.S. trade competitors, such as Japan, seemed to have developed an effective economic model different in important respects from what many Americans believed to be the traditional laissez-faire U.S. approach.[74] A key feature of that model was its emphasis on cooperation between government and industry rather than competition. The ability of different arms of Japanese industry to work with one another, and the close relationship between government and industry in supporting key economic sectors, appeared to have created substantial benefits for the Japanese economy.[75]

The mixed record of the large-scale demonstration projects of the 1970s and the perceived success of the government-industry cooperation in Japan led to a shift in U.S. policy in the 1980s.[76] One of the strategies adopted by the United

[73]Questions persist concerning the degree of the U.S. decline in the 1980s, just as questions remain concerning the current business cycle. The STEP Board review of the competitive resurgence of the U.S. economy includes an assessment of the factors that have contributed to the U.S. recovery with a focus on eleven U.S. manufacturing and service sectors. See National Research Council, *U.S. Industry in 2000: Studies in Competitive Performance, op. cit.*

[74]For a discussion of the different economic and cultural assumptions underpinning these differences, see Clyde V. Prestowitz, *Trading Places*, New York: Basic Books, 1988, Chapter 5; and James Fallows, *Looking at the Sun: The Rise of the New East Asian Economic and Political System*, New York: Pantheon Books, 1994, Chapter 4, pp. 194, 210. For an overview of these issues, see National Research Council, *Conflict and Cooperation,* 1996, *op. cit.,* pp. 12-40. For a review of the main features of the East Asian economic success story, see World Bank, *The East Asian Economic Miracle: Economic Growth and Public Policy,* Policy Research Report, New York: Oxford University Press, 1993.

[75]For the best early analysis of the Japanese approach, see Chalmers Johnson, *MITI and the Japanese Miracle: The Growth of Industrial Policy 1925-1975,* Stanford, CA: Stanford University Press, 1982. See also D.T. Okimoto, "The Japanese Challenge in High Technology Industry," in National Research Council, *The Positive Sum Strategy*, R. Landau and N. Rosenberg, eds., Washington, D.C.: National Academy Press, 1986; and D.T. Okimoto, *MITI and the Market: Japanese Industrial Policy for High Technology Industry*, Stanford, CA: Stanford University Press, 1989.

[76]Michael Borrus and Jay Stowsky observe that many partnerships have been successful, but there are also "outright flops like the supersonic transport, synfuel plants and the fast breeder reactor, as well as more ambiguous cases like the development of numerical control (NC) for machine tools or of photovoltaics. The supersonic transport (SST) failed because the commercial airliner market was aiming at short-haul and wide-bodies rather than supersonic speeds. The fast breeder reactor and synfuel programs were far more expensive than commercial alternatives, particularly after the oil shocks abated. In each case there were problems of both conception and execution: performance objectives were narrowly construed and alternative technological paths were not sufficiently explored. Demonstrations and pilots proceeded despite experimental evidence of failure. In some cases, like photovoltaics, political considerations killed development prematurely. See Michael Borrus and Jay Stowsky, "Technology Policy and Economic Growth," in *Investing in Innovation*, Lewis M. Branscomb and James H. Keller, eds., Cambridge, MA: MIT Press, 1999.

States in response to its perceived loss in competitiveness was to encourage greater cooperation within industry and between industry and government. Most federal support for industry before the mid-1980s took the form of research grants or contracts for product development or procurement that often included substantial support for research.[77] In the latter half of the decade a growing number of programs were established based on partnerships among government, industry, and universities. Indeed, the 1980s and early 1990s saw a conscious effort to expand cooperation, in part by using federal R&D funding more effectively to meet what were seen as unprecedented competitive challenges.

In addition to SEMATECH, which matched substantial federal and industry funding in a consortium of semiconductor manufacturers,[78] these partnerships included the Semiconductor Research Corporation, which pools industry and limited federal funding to support university research in semiconductors, NSF engineering research centers, which involve industry-university cooperation on engineering problems, expanded CRADAs, and extramural programs at the National Institute of Standards and Technology.[79]

These public and private initiatives undertaken in the 1980s demonstrated a renewed emphasis on cooperation in U.S. public policy. In the latter part of that decade there was an increasing emphasis on public-private partnerships. Some, such as the Advanced Technology Program, were characterized by competitive awards of fixed duration. Facilitating these policy experiments were a number of major legislative initiatives passed by Congress. These are highlighted in Box G.

---

[77]National Research Council, Funding a Revolution, *op. cit.*, pp. 32-33.

[78]In 1996, SEMATECH became a completely private-sector consortium. In 2000, it became International SEMATECH, a consortium that includes companies from both Asia and Europe.

[79]Some of the other major federal partnerships of this period were DOD's Manufacturing Technology (MANTECH) program; the Department of Transportation's Intelligent Vehicle Highway Systems (IVHS) program and National Magnetic Levitation initiative (MAGLEV); the NSF's Research Centers program (which includes the engineering research centers, the industry/university cooperative research centers, the materials research science and engineering centers, and the science and technology centers); and the Small Business Technology Transfer (STTR) program. See Coburn and Berglund, *Partnerships*, *op. cit.*, p. 488.

Box G. Principal Federal Legislation Related to Cooperative Technology Programs[81]

- **Stevenson-Wydler Technology Innovation Act (1980).** This Act required federal laboratories to facilitate the transfer of federally owned and originated technology to state and local governments and the private sector. The Act includes a requirement that each federal lab spend a specified percentage of its research and development budget on transfer activities and that an Office of Research and Technology Applications (ORTA) be established to facilitate such transfer.
- **Bayh-Dole University and Small Business Patent Act (1980).** This Act permitted government grantees and contractors to retain title to federally funded inventions and encouraged universities to license inventions to industry. The Act is designed to foster interaction between universities and the business community and provided, in part, for title to inventions made by contractors receiving federal R&D funds to be vested in the contractor if they are small businesses, universities, or not-for-profit institutions.
- **Small Business Innovation Development Act (1982).** This Act established the Small Business Innovation Research (SBIR) Program within the major federal R&D agencies to increase government funding of research with commercialization potential in the small high-technology company sector. Each federal agency with an R&D budget of $100 million or more is required to set aside a certain percentage of that amount to finance the SBIR effort.
- **National Cooperative Research Act (1984).** This Act eased antitrust penalties on cooperative research by instituting single, instead of treble, damages for antitrust violations in joint research. The Act also mandated a "rule of reason" standard for assessing potential antitrust violations for cooperative research. This contrasted with the per se standard by which any R&D collusion is an automatic violation, regardless of a determination of economic damage.
- **Federal Technology Transfer Act (1986).** This Act amended the Stevenson-Wydler Technology Innovation Act to authorize CRADAS between federal laboratories and other entities, including state agencies.
- **Omnibus Trade and Competitiveness Act (1988).** This Act established the Competitiveness Policy Council and created several new programs. (Among these are the Advanced Technology program and the manufacturing technology centers.) These are housed in the Department of Commerce's National Institute of Standards and Technology and are intended to help commercialize promising new technologies and to improve manufacturing techniques of small and medium-size manufacturers.

---

[80]Adapted with NRC modifications from Berglund and Coburn, *op. cit.*, p. 485.

- **National Competitiveness Technology Transfer Act (1989).** Part of the DOD authorization bill, this act amended the Stevenson-Wydler Act to allow government-owned, contractor-operated laboratories to enter into cooperative R&D agreements.
- **Defense Conversion, Reinvestment, and Transition Assistance Act (1992).** This Act initiated the Technology Reinvestment Project (TRP) to establish cooperative, interagency efforts that address the technology development, deployment, and education and training needs within both the commercial and defense communities.
- **Small Business Technology Transfer Act (1992).** This act established the Small Business Technology Transfer program (STTR), which seeks to increase private sector commercialization of technology developed through Federal R&D. The program encourages research partners at universities and other non-profit research institutions to enter formal collaborative relationships with the small business concerns. Federal agencies with extramural R&D budgets over $1 billion are required to administer STTR programs using an annual set-aside of 0.15 percent. The set-aside will increase to 0.3 percent in FY2004.

Problems That Small Businesses Face in Financing Growth

In addition to the growing recognition of the importance of small business for innovation and employment, there is also today a better understanding of the problems that small businesses face in financing growth. One type of problem has to do with information asymmetries in the market for startup financing. As Joshua Lerner has pointed out, asymmetries in information between entrepreneurs and financiers are likely to work to the disadvantage of small firms.[81] Even though providers of funds have strong incentives to gather information about the small business in which they may be investing, the entrepreneur—especially in technology startups—is likely to be the only person with in-depth knowledge of the technology and the market opportunity. Moreover, that knowledge is likely to be insufficient to perfectly predict potential payoffs. The result is "statistical discrimination" whereby financiers are motivated to withhold funds, even for promising opportunities, because it is too costly—and often impossible—to gather the information needed to assess potential investment payoffs.[82]

[81]See Joshua Lerner, "Public Venture Capital: Rationale and Evaluation" in National Research Council, *The Small Business Innovation Research Program, Challenges and Opportunities*, C. Wessner, ed., Washington, D.C.: National Academy Press, 1999, Appendix A.

[82]*Ibid.*

A second problem involves the appropriability of R&D results. The economics literature has long recognized that knowledge is "leaky," that is, new knowledge often transcends the boundaries of firms and intellectual property protection, so that the creator of that knowledge cannot fully capture the economic value of the knowledge through the price system.[83] Moreover, several case studies of small businesses suggest that appropriability problems may be particularly acute for small businesses.[84] In other words, R&D-generated innovations may escape the organizational walls of small firms with relatively greater ease than large businesses.[85] At the same time ideas not valued and pursued in one firm are often the reason an entrepreneur starts a new firm.[86]

A third problem stems from asymmetries in the availability of capital. Private equity markets are characterized by two substantial funding gaps. The first gap occurs primarily in the seed and start-up financing stage. This gap ranges from $100,000 at the low end, the point at which the money raised from friends and families and bootstrapping runs out, to the $2 million range on the high end, the time when the venture would historically become attractive enough to catch the eye of venture fund investors. The second market gap occurs in the early stage of equity financing. While the venture capital industry has progressed to larger and later-stage financing, the informal market has remained active below the $2 million threshold. As a result, a capital gap in the $2 million to $5 million range has developed.[87]

These larger capital requirements, still considered early-stage deals, have spawned a new hybrid of angel financing—the angel alliance. These alliances represent relatively large groups of business angels willing to fund some second round, early-stage deals. In addition, some of the capital requirements in this secondary gap have been met through co-investment between private investors and early-stage financing entities.[88]

The Committee's study of the SBIR program and ATP highlight specific issues related to the performance of public-private partnerships for which the federal government provides innovation funding to help small firms overcome early-stage financing hurdles. The role of assessment, taken up in the next section, follows a summary below of the features of the SBIR and ATP programs.

---

[83]See Edwin Mansfield, "How Fast Does New Industrial Technology Leak Out?" *Journal of Industrial Economics*, 34(2):217-224 for a discussion of the rationale for firms locating R&D facilities in foreign countries, one of which is to absorb leaky R&D information from firms in those countries.

[84]See Lerner, *op. cit.*

[85]*Ibid.*

[86]See David Audretsch, *Innovation and Industry Evolution*. Cambridge, MA: MIT Press, 1995.

[87]See Jeffery E. Sohl, "The Early-Stage Equity Market in the USA," *Venture Capital* 1(2), 1999. See also by the same author, "The Private Equity Market in the U.S.: What a Long Strange Trip It Has Been." Mimeo, Whittemore School of Business and Economics, University of New Hampshire, 2002.

[88]John May, "Angel Alliances and Angel Practices." Presented at The State of the Angel Market Workshop, Boston, MA, March 27, 2002.

The Small Business Innovation Research Program

SBIR was established in 1982 as a way to channel federal research and development funds to small businesses, while meeting mission needs of various government agencies through the use of research and development (R&D) expertise that is often unique to small businesses.[89] The SBIR grant-making process is structured in three phases. Phase I constitutes a feasibility study in which award winners undertake a limited amount of research aimed at establishing an idea's scientific and commercial promise. Today Phase I grants can be as high as $100,000. Phase II grants are larger—normally $750,000—and fund more extensive R&D. It is intended to develop the scientific and technical merit and the feasibility of research ideas. In Phase III, which normally does not involve SBIR funds, grant recipients should be obtaining additional funds either from an interested agency, private investors, or the capital markets to move the technology to the prototype stage and into the marketplace.

Initially the SBIR program required agencies with R&D budgets in excess of $100 million to set aside 0.2 percent of their funds for SBIR. This totaled $45 million in 1983, the program's first year of operation. Over the next six years the set-aside percentage grew to 1.25 percent. In 1992 Congress renewed the program and doubled the set-aside rate from 1.25 percent to 2.5 percent.[90] For fiscal year 2000 this resulted in a program budget of approximately $1.2 billion across all federal agencies, with the DOD having the largest SBIR program at $554 million, followed by the National Institutes of Health (NIH) at $362 million.[91] Since 1982, over $10 billion has been awarded to various small businesses through the SBIR program.[92]

Congress's reauthorization of the SBIR program in 1992 resulted in the set-aside being raised from 1.25 percent to 2.5 percent. This increase was consistent with a recommendation from the National Academy of Sciences to increase SBIR funding as a means of improving the U.S. economy's ability to adopt and commercialize new technologies.[93] By 1992 the SBIR program had also become po-

---

[89] See George Brown and James Turner, "The Federal Role in Small Business Research," *Issues in Science and Technology,* Summer, 1999, p. 52.

[90] The Small Business Research and Development Enhancement Act, P.L. 102-564, October 28, 1992.

[91] See <http://www.acq.osd.mil/sadbu/sbir/overview.htm> for information on the DOD's SBIR program. For information on NIH's SBIR program, see <http://grants.nih.gov/grants/funding/sbir.htm#sbir>.

[92] *Ibid.*

[93] The Committee on Science, Engineering, and Public Policy of the National Academy of Sciences noted that "Congress should consider legislation to increase the agency SBIR set-aside. The program should be expanded so that more companies can participate in it." See National Research Council, *The Government Role in Civilian Technology: Building A New Alliance,* Washington, D.C.: National Academy Press, 1992, p. 65.

litically popular with increasingly influential small business advocates. In conjunction with the emergence of innovative small startups in computing, biotechnology, and advanced materials, there was ample support for program expansion in 1992.[94] Most recently the Small Business Reauthorization Act of 2000 (P.L. 106-554) extended the program for a further eight years, while mandating in Section 108 of the legislation that the National Research Council conduct a comprehensive review of how the program has stimulated technological innovation and used small businesses to meet federal research and development needs.[95]

The Advanced Technology Program

The Advanced Technology Program describes its mission as "bridging the gap between the research lab and the marketplace."[96] Specifically the ATP provides cost-shared funding to industry intended to accelerate the development and dissemination of high-risk technologies with the potential for broad-based economic benefits for the U.S. economy.[97] The ATP funding is directed to technical research (but not product development). Companies, whether singly or jointly, conceive, propose, and execute all projects, often in collaboration with universities and federal laboratories. The ATP shares the project costs for a limited time. Single-company awardees can receive up to $2 million for R&D activities for up to three years. Larger companies must contribute at least 60 percent of the total project cost. Joint ventures can receive funds for R&D activities for up to five years.[98]

---

[94]See Brown and Turner, op. cit., p. 53. In addition to an account of SBIR's evolution Brown and Turner offer constructive criticisms of the SBIR program and recommendations for improvement.

[95]This study is mandated under Section 108 of HR5667, The Small Business Reauthorization Act of 2000 (Public Law 106-554). It calls for a review of the SBIR programs of the DOD, Department of Energy, NIH, NSF, and NASA with regard to such parameters as the quality of the research projects being conducted under the SBIR program, the commercialization of the research, and the program's contribution to accomplishing agency missions. The evaluation is also expected to include estimates of the benefits, both economic and non-economic, achieved by the SBIR program, as well as broader policy issues associated with public-private collaborations for technology development and government support for high-technology innovation, including benchmarking of foreign programs to encourage small business development. The assessment is to gauge the contributions of the SBIR program with regard to economic growth, technology development, and commercialization, and contributions by small business awardees to the accomplishment of agency missions. The review will also seek to identify best practices and operational improvements for the SBIR program.

[96]See the ATP Web site <http://www.atp.nist.gov/atp/overview.htm>.

[97]See National Research Council, *The Advanced Technology Program, Challenges and Opportunities*, C. Wessner, ed, Washington, D.C.: National Academy Press, 1999.

[98]See National Research Council, *The Advanced Technology Program, Assessing Outcomes, op. cit.*

ATP was initiated as a means of funding high-risk R&D with broad commercial and societal benefits that would not be undertaken by a single company, either because the risk was too high or because a large enough share of the benefits of success would not accrue to the company for it to make the investment. ATP lacked the straightforward national security rationale that had underpinned many postwar U.S. technology programs. It did reflect, however, a general trend away from purely mission-oriented research and development toward more broadly based technological advances.

For the 41 competitions held 1990-2000 ATP made 522 awards for approximately $1.64 billion. These awards went to 1,162 participating organizations and an approximately equal number of subcontractors. Universities and non-profit independent research organizations play a significant role as participants in ATP projects. Universities have participated in over half of the projects, involving more than 176 individual universities.[99] Indeed, recent Administration proposals to improve the program call for a greater role for universities.[100]

With peer-reviewed competitions, the ATP supports the development of a wide variety of new technologies. These have included adaptive learning systems, component-based software, digital data storage, information infrastructure for health care, microelectronics manufacturing infrastructure, manufacturing technology for photonics, motor vehicles and printed wiring boards, new tissue-engineering technologies, bio-polymer repairs, and tools for DNA diagnostics.[101] These technologies are technically promising but commercially risky. This means that significant portions of the ATP-funded projects are likely to fail.[102] This is to be expected; no failures would suggest insufficient risk. At the same time, recent research suggests that a significant portion are succeeding.[103] The results of some projects, such as ATP's early support for extreme ultraviolet (EUV) lithography research, have made significant contributions to the development of next generation lithography.[104]

[99]See Alan P. Balutis and Barbara Lambis, "The ATP Competition Structure" in National Research Council, *The Advanced Technology Program, Assessing Outcomes, op. cit.*

[100]See U.S. Department of Commerce, "The Advanced Technology Program: Reform with a Purpose," February 2002. The proposals made by the Secretary of Commerce do not call for the abolition of the program; instead, the report makes six proposals to improve the program. Most of these are consistent with the Committee's assessment; others may prove difficult to implement. The administrative initiative represents a major step toward a positive consensus on the program's value.

[101]See Alan P. Balutis and Barbara Lambis, *op. cit.* See also Rosalie Ruegg, "Taking a Step Back: An Early Results Overview of Fifty ATP Awards" in National Research Council, *The Advanced Technology Program, Assessing Outcomes, op. cit.*

[102]This federal partnership program is exceptional in that it identifies and declares failures.

[103]See Rosalie Ruegg, *op. cit.*

[104]Interestingly, the value of the ATP-funded work did not become immediately apparent. As such, it represents an example of the indirect path of a project 's trajectory. See the paper by Rosalie Ruegg in National Research Council, *Advanced Technology Program; Measuring Outcomes, op. cit.*

Box H. Critical Characteristics of the Advanced Technology Program

Independent researchers have summarized ATP's "critical characteristics" that differentiate it from other government R&D programs.

- A focus on developing the economic benefit of early-stage, high-risk, enabling innovative civilian technologies.
- Emphasis on the formation of partnerships and consortia that facilitate the diffusion of innovation.
- Rigorous, competitive selection process with an independent evaluation of the project's technical merit, commercial worthiness, and potential for broad-based economic benefits.
- Debriefings for those firms that apply but are not selected.

Research led by Professor Maryann Feldman of Johns Hopkins University and Maryellen Kelly, formerly of Carnegie Mellon University, is particularly important in that it focuses on the ATP contribution to private-sector innovation.[105] Feldman and Kelly identify the following characteristics of ATP:

ATP funding does not displace private capital. Using data from a survey of 1998 ATP applicants, the study finds that most of the non-winners did not proceed with any aspect of their proposed R&D project, and of those that did, most did so on a smaller scale than initially proposed. This suggests that ATP funding is not simply displacing private capital.

The program received high marks from its users. A substantial majority of the applicants surveyed by Feldman and Kelley considered ATP's application process fair and rational.

High spillover potential. The survey finds that the projects and firms selected by ATP are more willing than those not selected to share their research findings with other firms and tend to be collaborative in new technical areas and form new R&D partnerships—findings consistent with ATP's goal of selecting projects with high spillover potential.

"Halo Effect." The study also finds that the ATP award can create a "halo effect" for recipients, increasing the success of award recipients in attracting additional funding from other sources, an effect documented by several earlier researchers.[106]

Feldman and Kelley conclude that the ATP is leveraging activities that have the potential to contribute to broad-based economic growth.

---

[105]See Maryann P. Feldman and Maryellen R. Kelley, "Leveraging Research and Development: The Impact of the Advanced Technology Program," in National Research Council, *The Advanced Technology Program: Assessing Outcomes, op. cit.*, pp. 189-210.

[106]See Silber & Associates, *Survey of Advanced Technology Program 1990-1992 Awardees: Company Opinion about the ATP and its Early Effects,* NIST GCR 97-707, February 1996; and Solomon Associates, *Advanced Technology Program: An Assessment of Short-Term Impacts—First Competition Participants,* February 1993. Based on his research on the SBIR program, Joshua Lerner describes this as a "certification effect." See J. Lerner, "'Public Venture Capital': Rationales and Evaluation," in National Research Council, *The Small Business Innovation Research Program: Challenges and Opportunities, op. cit.*, pp. 115-128.

IV

ACCOUNTABILITY AND ASSESSMENT

Accountability and Assessment

THE NEED FOR GOALS, METRICS, AND ASSESSMENT

In many high-technology industries the burgeoning development costs for new technologies, the dispersal of technological expertise, and the growing importance of regulatory and environmental issues provide powerful incentives to form government-industry-university partnerships. Even though policy makers have yet to arrive at a consensus on the issue, cooperative programs reflecting public-private partnerships have expanded substantially. SEMATECH was established under the Reagan Administration after much debate.[1] The first Bush Administration saw the creation of the Advanced Technology Program (ATP) within the National Institute of Standards and Technology. The Clinton Administration came to office with an emphasis on civilian technology programs, substantially expanding the ATP and creating the Technology Reinvestment Project (TRP).[2] The rapid expansion of these programs generated significant opposition, rekindling the national debate on the appropriate role of the government in fostering new technologies.

---

[1]For an overview of SEMATECH, see National Research Council, *Securing the Future: Regional and National Programs to Support the Semiconductor Industry, op. cit.* For a comprehensive assessment of SEMATECH in comparison with MCC, see John B. Horrigan, *op. cit.*

[2]For an analysis of ATP, see National Research Council, *The Advanced Technology Program, Challenges and Opportunities, op. cit.*, and National Research Council, *The Advanced Technology Program, Assessing Outcomes, op. cit.* For an excellent analysis of the TRP, see Jay Stowsky, "Politics and Policy: The Technology Reinvestment Program and the Dilemmas of Dual Use." Mimeo, University of California, 1996. See also, Linda R. Cohen, "Dual-use and the Technology Reinvestment Project," in Branscomb and Keller, *op. cit.*, pp. 174-193.

Broader philosophical questions about the appropriate role for government in partnership with industry have tended to obscure the need for policy makers to draw lessons from current and previous cooperative efforts. A virtue of the study of partnerships is that it has not addressed the ideological debates that often have obscured the need for careful analysis of the structure, goals, mechanisms, and metrics for measuring the success of a public-private partnership. Such measurement of success is often analytically difficult, particularly in the absence of a clear articulation of program goals and metrics. As we illustrated with the case of S&T parks, the goals of partnerships often vary. Consequently, the standards by which we are to gauge their success also vary.[3] This is why it is so important to include an assessment program as an integral part of the organization of a partnership.

Programs such as the ATP, which incorporate a rigorous, competitive selection process with an independent evaluation of the project's technical merit, commercial worthiness, and potential for broad-based economic benefits, serve as a model in this respect. As the results of the assessment activity are integrated more and more into the operations of the programs, the knowledge generated helps the partnership adapt in ways that foster better results. Similarly, an important contribution of this NRC analysis is to inform U.S. policy by providing a pragmatic, results-oriented perspective. To this end, the study has applied a variety of economic assessment methods to partnership activity, ranging from laboratory S&T parks to the accomplishments of the SBIR program. These techniques are described below.

The Role of Analysis

The analysis of public-private partnerships is of growing importance, given the considerable change in federal research and development budgets since the end of the Cold War and the reduced role of many centralized laboratories in the private sector.[4] Such analysis has a variety of functions.

- *Analysis—rather than doctrinal claims—contributes to a better appreciation of the role of partnerships between government and industry in the development of the U.S. economy.*

  Writing 20 years ago, Richard Nelson of Columbia University observed that Americans are still remarkably uninformed about the long history of policies aimed at stimulating innovation.[5] The past decade has seen the

[3]See Michael Luger and Harvey Goldstein, *Technology in the Garden, Research Parks and Regional Economic Development, op. cit.*

[4]See Richard Rosenbloom and William Spencer, *Engines of Innovation: U.S. Industrial Research at the End of an Era*, 1996, *op. cit.*

[5]See Otis L. Graham, *Losing Time: The Industrial Policy Debate.* Cambridge, MA: Harvard University Press, 1992, p. 250. Graham cites Richard Nelson's observations at the end of the Carter

introduction of the geo-positioning satellite, the Internet, and the genome revolution—innovations that are changing how we live and are affecting the prospects for economic advance. Even so, a recent comprehensive report on government support for computing research opens by stating that it is "difficult to recall and acknowledge" the federal government's major role in launching and sustaining the computer revolution, both in terms of innovation and infrastructure.[6] While many Americans appreciate the contribution of technology to robust economic growth, there is little evidence that they are aware of the major contributions—from radio to the Internet—of federal support for technological innovation.[7]

- *Analysis can help to inform the public and policy makers of the risks and opportunities involved in government support.*
  Perhaps a more compelling argument for assessment is that government involvement in market processes is fraught with risk. There are cases of major successes resulting from federal support of the computer or semiconductor industries, where the Department of Defense served as a source of R&D and as a reliable, early buyer of products.[8] There are also cases of major frustration; illustrative landmarks here would include projects such as the supersonic transport, the Synfuels Corporation, and the Clinch River breeder reactor. [9] These were open-ended, large-scale demonstration projects quite different from the limited time and funding allocated to

---

Administration. The situation may not have improved. Writing in 1994, James Fallows makes a similar observation (see *Looking into the Sun: The Rise of the New East Asian Economic and Political System.* New York: Pantheon Books, 1994, p. 196). See also Thomas McCraw's "Mercantilism and the Market: Antecedents of American Industrial Policy," in *The Politics of Industrial Policy,* Claude E. Barfield and William A. Schambra, eds., Washington, D.C.: American Enterprise Institute for Public Policy Research, 1986, pp. 33-62.

[6]See National Research Council, *Funding a Revolution: Government Support for Computing Research, op. cit,* p. 1.

[7]*Ibid.,* pp. 85-135 and pp. 169-83. The report provides a thorough review of government support for computers, the Internet, and related technologies and infrastructure.

[8]See Graham, *op. cit.,* p. 2.

[9]These programs are frequently cited as failures, though in many cases the merit of these claims are difficult to assess, not least because contemporary political developments shape outcomes and the subsequent perceptions can color the assessments of these programs. Linda Cohen and Roger Noll present an interesting review of technology development programs, mainly from the 1970s. Their analysis is less negative than the title suggests. The volume identifies successful R&D projects, such as the photovoltaic electricity program and the authors point out that government support for a wide range of technologies has proved to have had a positive impact. See Cohen and Noll, *The Technology Pork Barrel, op. cit.,* pp. 97, 178, 217-320. The programs reviewed here reflect the policy lessons of the 1970s; current partnerships tend to be much smaller in scope, limited in time, and often require cost share as a means of preventing open-ended commitments.

partnerships today. Analysis of the elements of these failures has contributed to policy changes.

The development of cooperative mechanisms for partnering on advanced R&D is indeed desirable. This is because, looked at as a whole, the opportunities from effective partnerships greatly outweigh the risks. Failures will (and do) occur. Yet federal funding of research and development has led to such advances as atomic energy, the Internet, the Global Positioning System, lasers, solar-electric cells, communications satellites, jet aircraft, genetic medicine, and a wide array of advanced materials and composites.[10] Even critics of some technology programs are careful to note that the overall result of public support of new technologies has been highly positive.[11] They recognize that government support for a wide range of technologies has helped build the foundations of the modern economy.[12]

The Need for Regular Assessments

These successes demonstrate the promise of "game changing" technologies, like wide-body jets, satellites, and—of course—the Internet. Yet, however profound, these successes in no way negate the need for regular assessments. Technology development is inherently risky. Promising projects will fail. The commitment of public funds requires that realistic but effective assessments be regularly undertaken.

- Regular assessment through cost-sharing requirements with private funds can serve as an effective means to ensure continued technical viability.
- Assessment can also help guard against the "political capture" of projects, as occurred with some of the large commercial demonstration efforts of the 1970s.[13]
- Even successful partnerships face the challenge of adapting programs to rapidly changing technologies.[14] Assessment thus becomes a means of keeping programs technologically and commercially relevant.

---

[10]Office of Science and Technology Policy, *Fact Sheet on How Federal R&D Investments Drive the U.S. Economy*, Executive Office of the President, June 15, 2000, <http://www-es.ucsd.edu/stpp/whouse(rp).htm#06153.doc>.

[11]See Cohen and Noll, *The Technology Pork Barrel, op. cit.*, p. 3.

[12]*Ibid.*

[13]*Ibid.*, pp. 242-257, Cohen and Noll stress that political capture by distributive congressional politics and industrial interests are one of the principal risks for government-supported commercialization projects. In cases such as the Clinch River project, they extensively document the disconnect between declining technical feasibility and increasing political support. Shared-cost partnerships of limited duration address this risk.

[14]One of the strengths of SEMATECH was its ability to redefine goals in the face of changing conditions. See National Research Council, 1996, *op. cit.*, p. 148. See also Grindley, et al., "SEMATECH and Collaborative Research: Lessons in the Design of High-technology Consortia," *Journal of Policy Analysis and Management,* 1994, p. 724.

- Assessment also reminds policy makers of the need for humility before the "black box" of innovation. As one informed observer notes, "Experience argues for hedged commitments, constant reappraisal, maintenance of options, pluralism of advice and decision makers."[15]

"Picking Winners and Losers?"

In the United States, discussions of best practices concerning partnerships between the government, industry, and universities often include statements to the effect that the government cannot—or should not—"pick winners or losers." Many of these arguments have been articulated with regard to the relatively modest, but high profile Advanced Technology Program at the Department of Commerce. For example, a recent General Accounting Office study described two views of the ATP as follows: "ATP is seen by some as a means of addressing market failure in research areas that would otherwise not be funded, thereby facilitating the economic growth that comes from the commercialization and use of new technologies in the private sector." Advocates of programs such as the ATP believe that the government should serve as a catalyst for companies to cooperate and undertake important new work that would not have been possible in the same period without federal participation. Critics of the program view the same arrangement as industrial policy, or the means by which the government rather than the marketplace picks winners and losers.[16]

The use of the expression "picking winners and losers" does little to advance understanding of U.S. policy, often obscuring more than clarifying the issues associated with public-private partnership.[17] Generally, the expression means that:

---

[15]See Otis L. Graham, *Losing Time: The Industrial Policy Debate, op. cit.*, p. 251. Graham is referring to work by Richard R. Nelson in *Government and Technological Progress*, New York: Pergamon Press, 1982, p. 454-455.

[16]U.S. General Accounting Office, *Advanced Technology Program: Inherent Factors in Selection Process Could Limit Identification of Similar Research, op. cit.*, p. 5.

[17]As with the private sector, the government's judgment and capability do not insulate it from failure. Both the private sector and the government face the same uncertainties. Each must place bets, albeit for different reasons. Each cannot avoid the certainty of loss. Each can cover enough points to be assured of some winners. "In short, winners and losers are an inevitable by-product of the process of innovation. Picking winners and losers is the wrong metaphor to characterize the socially useful and necessary activity of government in supporting that process. Government is actually placing bets on our collective future, and from the public standpoint, the magnitude of the potential social gains are sufficiently large to provide a comfortable margin for error in choosing among technologies to back." See the testimony of Professor Michael Borrus, University of California at Berkeley, before the House of Representatives Committee on Science, Subcommittee on Technology, April 10, 1997, <http://www.house.gov/science/borrus_4-10.html>.

- The government does not have the capability to make judgments concerning new technologies or firms;
- The government should not substitute its judgment for that of the market by selecting among technologies or firms;
- Government intervention in the market is unwarranted and constitutes a form of corporate welfare.[18]

These arguments are obviously interrelated, and their appeal is grounded in the popular perception of a U.S. economy regularly transformed by individual investors and entrepreneurs. This view of the role of entrepreneurs is well founded, of course, both in terms of American economic history and in terms of today's economy.

Yet, it is equally true that the federal government has long played a nurturing role; indeed, the U.S. innovation system is the result of a complex interaction of public and private initiative. Arguments that do not consider this interaction ignore important aspects of the history of technology development in the United States. They also fail to reflect key elements of recent and current practice that have played critical roles in the development of such platform technologies as the Internet, contributed to such enabling technologies as semiconductors, or supported research and development in the pharmaceutical, medical device, and biomedical industries.[19]

Further, the government has demonstrated a capacity to make judgments with respect to new technologies. It has been instrumental in developing major new

---

[18]See, for example, the testimony by Edward L. Hudgins before the Senate Committee on Commerce, Science, and Transportation, August 1, 1995. In addition to recommending the abolishment of the Department of Commerce and NIST, Hudgins argues that "in the area of advanced commercial technologies, that is, the high-tech revolution of the past 15 years, the private sector already does a world-class job in developing new products and technologies. Thus, ATP is unnecessary. The way a competitive market system—as opposed to a corporatist or socialist system—works is that if there is a prospect for a profit, entrepreneurs will risk investing in order to reap profits. Not all entrepreneurs share this view. David Morgenthaler, for example, believes that [the ATP] is an excellent program for developing enabling, or platform, technologies, which can have broad applications but are long-term, risky investments. Venture capitalists are not going to fund these opportunities, because they will feel that they are at too early a stage of maturity. Government can and should fund these technologies. In fact, it should do more than it is doing."

[19]Public grants to non-profits and private companies constitute a significant portion of NIH funding. In FY2000 $1.0 billion, or nearly 7 percent, of NIH funding for research grants and R&D contracts went to for-profit organizations. An additional $1.4 billion, or 10 percent, went to non-profit institutes, some of which are reported to be closely associated with for-profit firms. For NIH funding by performer in FY2000, see <http://silk.nih.gov/public/cbz2zoz.@www.trends00.fy9100.per.htm>. For increasing relationships between non-profit research institutions and for-profit firms, see Chris Adams, "Laboratory Hybrids: How Adroit Scientists Aid Biotech Companies with Taxpayer Money—NIH Grants Go to Nonprofits Tied to For-profit Firms Set up by Researchers," *Wall Street Journal*, January 30, 2001, A1.

industries through a variety of means, including awards for demonstration projects, provision of long-term R&D support (e.g., the National Advisory Committee for Aeronautics),[20] support of a regulatory framework, and provision of early assured markets through government procurement.

One of the great strengths of the U.S. economy is that the government sees its central role as an arbiter of economic competition among private actors. To a remarkable degree this is accurate, yet the fact remains that the government does intervene in the market in many ways, be it through the provision of R&D support, development of a favorable regulatory framework, or procurement decisions for technologies for government missions in defense, space exploration, and health.

The government role, of course, is not confined to investment incentives. Its role in infrastructure building, support for research—both early and applied—and for training are all integral parts of the government's support for economic growth. Although not without controversy, the exercise of government's regulatory responsibilities has played a key role in the computing and telecommunications industries. For example, antitrust actions in the 1950s were intended to facilitate the entry of other companies and more rapid innovation in the computer industry.[21] Since the Telecommunications Act of 1996, government and industry have been closely involved in an ongoing debate concerning the optimal regulatory regime.[22] In short, the government has demonstrated the capability to make judgments concerning new technologies; it also *must* make such decisions to carry out its various responsibilities.

The NRC's assessments of the SBIR and ATP programs have resulted in the development and application of useful methodologies. Moreover, the Committee's evaluations have contributed in significant ways to improved assessment standards. This NRC study's assessment of several programs are described below.

[20]Founded in 1915, NACA made major contributions to the development of aeronautics in the United States, as noted above, until 1958, when it was incorporated into NASA. NASA is continuing its research.

[21]National Research Council, *Funding a Revolution*, *op. cit.*, p. 33.

[22]Since the Telecommunications Act of 1996, P.L. No. 104-104, 110 Stat. 56 (1996), the stakes for firms with incumbent positions and startups with different technologies and business plans have been enormous. Some are seeking new spectrum allocations (or re-allocations), others regulatory support through active enforcement of the act. The government's role is a critical component in the competitive position of many firms.

ASSESSING SMALL BUSINESS INNOVATION RESEARCH: THE DEPARTMENT OF DEFENSE FAST TRACK

As noted above, the SBIR program sets aside 2.5 percent of the R&D budget for the 10 federal agencies with annual extramural R&D budgets above $100 million. While the Small Business Administration is charged with coordinating the SBIR program, the dispersal of the program across departments and agencies with very different missions and modes of operation results in considerable variation within a common program framework across agencies. As in the case of DOD and NIH, the missions the program supports also vary substantially. The 1992 mandate to increase the focus on commercialization has consequently generated a very diverse response.[23] One of the most important responses has come from the Department of Defense, which has the largest SBIR program.

Based on an earlier initiative by the Ballistic Missile Defense Organization (BMDO), the DOD in October 1995 launched what was called a broader Fast Track initiative to attract new firms and encourage commercialization of SBIR-funded technologies throughout the department.[24] Fast Track seeks to improve commercialization through preferential evaluation and efforts to close the funding gap that can develop between Phase I and Phase II grants. The time lag, from the conclusion of Phase I and the receipt of Phase II funds, can create cash-flow problems for small firms. The Fast Track pilot addresses the gap by providing expedited review and essentially continuous funding from Phase I to Phase II as long as applying firms can demonstrate that they have obtained third-party financing for their technology.[25]

Two years after the launch of the Fast Track initiative the Under Secretary of Defense asked the National Research Council's Board on Science, Technology,

---

[23]See Otis L. Graham, *Losing Time: The Industrial Policy Debate, op. cit.*

[24]Information about the DOD's Fast Track can be found at the following Web site: <http://www.acq.osd.mil/sadbu/sbir/overview/overview.htm#fasttrack>. As of April 2000, 164 Phase I projects had qualified for Fast Track by attracting the required investment. Ninety-five percent of these were selected for Phase II awards. By contrast, on average, only 40 percent of DOD Phase I projects are selected for Phase II. Because the survey of Fast Track companies reported in this volume focused on Fast Track firms that had advanced to Phase II, the survey was sent only to firms from the first Fast Track solicitation, FY1996, a total of 48 firms. However, surveys were also sent to early BMDO awardees that employed a similar approach.

[25]In this context third-party financing means that another company or government agency has agreed to invest in or purchase the SBIR firm's technology; it can also mean that a venture capitalist has committed to invest in the firm or that other private capital is available. The expedited decision-making process for the Phase II award is justified from the agency's perspective because outside funding validates the commercial promise of the technology. Some states have also developed innovative loan programs to address this gap. See <http://www.state.nj.us/scitech/sbirinfo.html> for a full description of the New Jersey program.

and Economic Policy (STEP) to assess Fast Track and related SBIR policy matters.[26] The Under Secretary's request focused on three issues.

- Whether Fast Track projects are achieving or appear likely to achieve greater success in SBIR than comparable non-Fast Track projects.
- Whether Fast Track projects progress at different rates than non-Fast Track projects.
- What do companies perceive as advantages and disadvantages of Fast Track participation.[27]

The request also permitted the Committee to review other issues relevant to the operation and performance of the SBIR program. Given the near absence of academic research on the SBIR program, it was necessary to commission field research on the program with a special emphasis on the Fast Track initiative. The research team assembled by the Committee examined the SBIR program awards and the Fast Track initiative from three perspectives:

- *Survey Research:* As a first step the research team developed a survey instrument and then commissioned an outside consulting firm experienced with the program to carry out a large-scale survey of DOD SBIR awardees, using a sample of firms that have participated in Fast Track and a control group. The roughly 300 firms[28] (294 firms doing 379 projects) queried constituted the largest survey to have focused on the Fast Track pilot. The survey response rate was high (reflecting the diligence with which the survey was pursued), with approximately 72 percent of the firms responding.
- *Case Studies:* In parallel, members of the research team conducted a series of case studies of SBIR companies, including when possible both Fast Track and non-Fast Track participants. The 55 case studies looked at firms in several major regions, such as New England, the southeast, and the southwest.
- *Empirical Analysis:* Using survey results and case studies, the researchers also examined whether SBIR-funded technologies would have been pursued without the SBIR award and what the social returns to SBIR-funded technologies were.

These case studies, surveys, and empirical research suggest that the Fast Track initiative is meeting its goals of encouraging commercialization and at-

[26]See National Research Council, *SBIR: An Assessment of the Department of Defense Fast Track Initiative, op. cit.*

[27]*Ibid.*

[28]*Ibid.* Separate surveys for each of the 379 projects were sent to 294 firms.

tracting new firms to the program. Consequently, the Committee recommended that Fast Track be continued and expanded where appropriate.[29] The Committee further noted that regular assessment of the SBIR program results and their comparison with the results of the Fast Track, both at DOD and at other participating agencies, would provide a valuable means of understanding the operation of this approximately $1.3-billion program. Such assessments of the program's efficiency and effectiveness were seen as even more critical given that the SBIR program budget is destined to increase.[30]

Surveys, case studies, and empirical analyses were also conducted in the Committee's assessment of the Advanced Technology Program, taken up next.

ASSESSING THE OPERATIONS OF THE ADVANCED TECHNOLOGY PROGRAM

The National Institute for Standards and Technology, in response to a request by the U.S. Senate, commissioned the National Academies to conduct an external review of the operations of the Advanced Technology program.[31] This ATP review was undertaken under the terms of reference of its study of government-industry partnerships.

The Committee's report noted that ATP's reliance on peer review—by both industry business experts and government technical experts—ensures to the extent possible the technical quality of proposals and thus enhances the potential for economic impact. At the same time, it noted that the requirement of a plan for commercialization—required in ATP proposals—encourages but cannot ensure a pathway to commercial development. Rather, it noted, the commercialization plan requirement is designed to ensure that projects that cannot offer at least a potential pathway to development are not supported with public funds.[32]

---

[29]*Ibid.*, See Recommendations and Findings.

[30]Although the research overseen by the Committee represents a significant step in improving our understanding of the SBIR program, these findings should be appreciated for what they are, that is, a preliminary and limited effort by independent researchers and an informed Committee to understand the operation of an important government-industry partnership. The Committee did not recommend that Fast Track be applied to the entire SBIR program at DoD, considering that to do so might put at risk other goals, such as research and concept development. Finally, the Committee recognized the need for additional research to validate these results over time For the complete Recommendations and Findings, see National Research Council, *SBIR: An Assessment of the Department of Defense Fast Track Initiative, op. cit.* Congress accepted this view and has mandated (under Section 108 of H.R. 5667 of the 106th Congress) that the National Research Council undertake additional research on the SBIR program.

[31]In Senate Report 105-235 the Advanced Technology Program was directed to arrange for a well-regarded organization with significant business and economic experience to conduct a comprehensive assessment of the ATP, analyzing how well the program has performed against the goals established in its authorizing statute, the Omnibus Trade and Competitiveness Act of 1988.

[32]For an overview of the ATP selection process, see the analysis by Alan P. Balutis and Barbara Lambis, "The ATP Competition Structure," *op. cit.* For an assessment of the impact of the program,

To avoid open-ended commitments of public funds to uncertain technologies the ATP has incorporated features that serve as reality checks, most notably, the matching expenditure of private funds by for-profit firms. This cost-share requirement, the limited financial commitment of the government through one-time awards, and the limited duration of the awards protect ATP against the criticism of open-ended government-led technology commercialization programs that some analysts believe characterized some of the major government initiatives of the 1970s and early 1980s.[33] Compared with these 1970s programs, ATP is a much smaller, more limited, and more focused effort with different mechanisms (e.g., one-time competitive awards) focused on technologies more likely to diffuse across the economy.[34] Its encouragement of company-university-laboratory cooperation and coordination with other public and private efforts is another distinguishing characteristic.[35] Its concept reflects the lessons of previous public policies and the recognition (discussed above) of the contributions small firms make in exploiting promising new technologies.

ATP's support for innovation, which is intended to generate significant spillovers yielding broad national economic benefits, has to be evaluated in the context of risks and benefits inherent in funding innovation. While its approach poses risks,[36] ATP's interest in enabling technologies with high spillover potential means that it is also a source of substantial potential benefit for the economy. By definition, the high-risk, high-payoff strategy means that many ATP projects will not achieve success.[37] The program deliberately seeks projects requiring the catalytic effect of a government award to bring together the industry-university partners to achieve significant technological advances.[38]

After an extensive assessment, the ATP was revealed to be an effective program—one that is achieving its legislated goals.[39] However, this partnership pro-

---

see the analysis by Maryann P. Feldman and Maryellen R. Kelley, "Leveraging Research and Development: The Impact of the Advanced Technology Program," *op. cit.*

[33]See Cohen and Noll, *op. cit.*

[34]Feldman and Kelley, *op. cit.*, find that projects and firms selected by the ATP are more willing to share their research findings and tend to be firms that open new paths of innovation by drawing on multiple technical areas through R&D partnerships.

[35]*Ibid.* Universities play a significant role in over half the ATP projects. See National Research Council, *The Advanced Technology Program: Assessing Outcomes, op. cit.*, p. 91.

[36]See Lewis Branscomb and Philip Auerswald, *Taking Technical Risks: How Innovators, Managers, and Investors Manage Risk in High-Tech Innovation*, Cambridge, MA: MIT Press, p. 145.

[37]ATP successes, insofar as they can be judged, are about 16 percent of the program—a rate comparable to venture capital programs that normally operate later in the development cycle. For an overview of the ATP record of achievement, see the analysis by Rosalie Ruegg, "Taking a Step Back: An Early Results Overview of Fifty ATP Awards," in National Research Council, *The Advanced Technology Program, Assessing Outcomes, op. cit.*

[38]See Jeffrey Dyer and Benjamin Powell, "Perspectives on the Determinants of Success in ATP-sponsored R&D Joint Ventures: The Views of Participants," in National Research Council, *The Advanced Technology Program, Assessing Outcomes, op. cit.*

[39]Following Senate report 105-235 NIST requested that the Board on Science, Technology, and

gram is one that could benefit from a more stable and robust funding.[40] ATP is best understood as one effective and valuable element of a national innovation system that employs a portfolio of policies and instruments to encourage the discovery, development, and exploitation of new technologies.[41] It is not a panacea for the challenges facing the U.S. economy. Rather, as the assessment carried out by the Government-Industry Partnerships Committee suggests, the ATP is achieving its goals with a degree of success commensurate with the technical and commercial difficulties associated with the program's objectives. Its awards hold the potential of advancing commercially and socially valuable technologies. As with any program, it could be improved, and the Committee's report recommended some ways to do so. It is also important to remember that the ATP carries out a much more rigorous review and assessment effort than any other U.S. partnership program. The Advanced Technology Program arguably represents a "best practice" in the United States in terms of the concept, management, regular assessment, and potential contributions.[42]

• • •

Whatever improvements might be made in the ATP and SBIR programs, the policy dialogue surrounding such programs certainly can be improved. Careful research, regular assessment, and attention to the initiatives under way around the world are more informative than sloganeering about "picking winners and losers."[43] A constructive dialogue about measures to capitalize on the substantial and growing U.S. R&D investment in areas of great promise needs to be advanced. Such a dialogue can help avoid misallocation of public funds and capture the substantial benefits of new technologies for the U.S. economy.

Economic Policy conduct an assessment of ATP in January 1999 as a part of its broader review of Government-Industry Partnerships for the Development of New Technologies.

[40]See National Research Council, *The Advanced Technology Program, Assessing Outcomes, op. cit.*, p. 94.

[41]See Richard R. Nelson, ed, *National Innovation System: A Comparative Study*, New York: Oxford University Press, 1993.

[42]See National Research Council, *The Advanced Technology Program, Assessing Outcomes, op. cit.*

[43]With regards to "winners and losers," the government's awards are in fact often made to firms in technologies that do not succeed (i.e., losers). This is normal. High-risk, potentially high-payout investments result in frequent failure, literally by definition. The ATP and SBIR programs also provide awards to firms with technologies that do succeed. These successes outweigh the costs of failed awards and permit advances in welfare growth and the success of national missions that would not otherwise occur in the same time frame, if at all.

VII

GLOBAL DIMENSIONS: COMPETITION AND COOPERATION

Global Dimensions: Competition and Cooperation

COMPARISONS IN A GLOBAL ECONOMY

From an international perspective, understanding the benefits and challenges of programs to support industry is important insofar as they have been and remain a central element in the national development strategies of both industrial and industrializing countries.

Governments around the world believe the composition of their economy matters. Accordingly, they have shown a great deal of imagination in their choices of mechanisms designed to support high-technology industries. To support industries and industrial companies based on new technologies many governments have active R&D programs and incentives. Some countries provide major financial support directly to national firms. In some cases this is done overtly through substantial direct grants, loans, loan guarantees, and public equity investments. In other cases, support is provided more opaquely through mechanisms such as tax deferrals, regional aid, worker training, or infrastructure development.[1] Some countries employ, as well, a wide range of trade policies from trade regulations designed to protect domestic products from foreign competition to tax rebates intended to stimulate the export of selected domestic products. The growing recognition of the role of science and high-technology industries in encouraging economic growth has led many governments to provide substantial R&D funding for enterprises of particular interest. In addition, as Figure 5 shows, many countries have substantially increased their overall national expenditures on R&D.

---

[1]For an overview of the policy goals and instruments, see National Research Council, *Conflict and Cooperation*, 1996, *op. cit.*, Box B, pp. 39-40. See also Martin Brown, *Impacts of National Technology Programs,* Paris: OECD, 1995, especially Chapter 2.

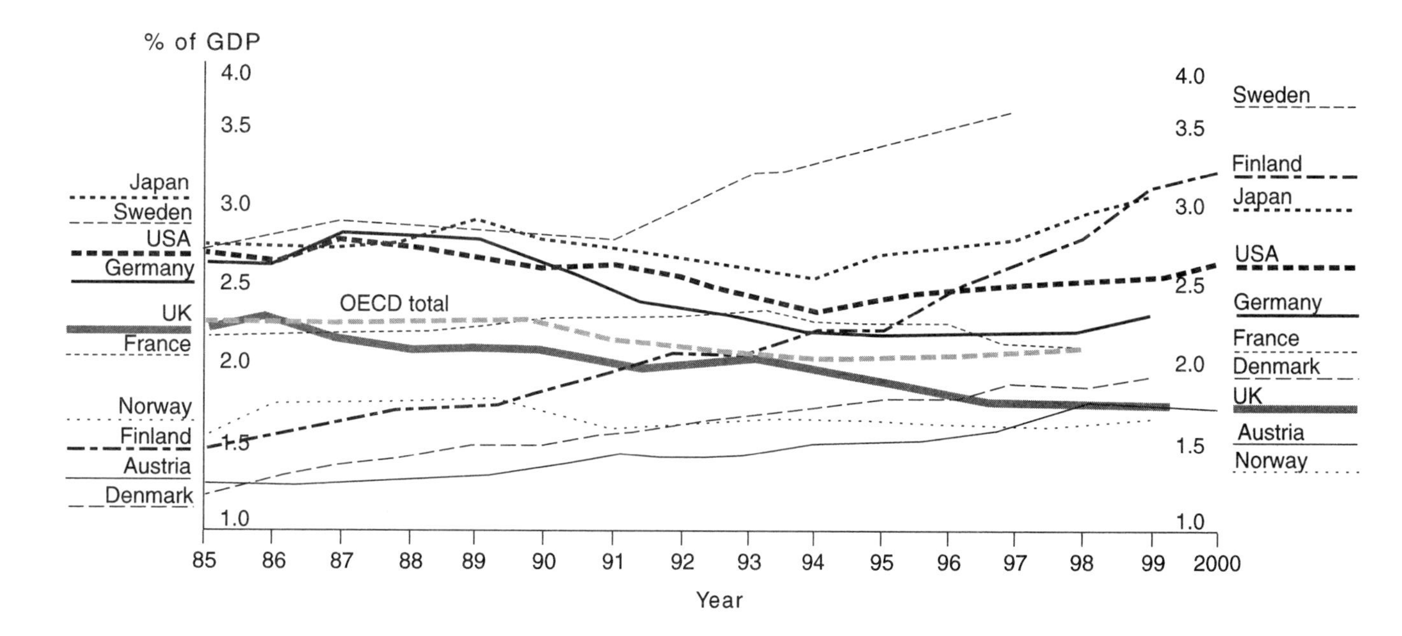

FIGURE 5 National expenditure on R&D.
Source: OECD, Main Science and Technology Indicators Database

Data collected by the Paris-based Organisation for Economic Co-operation and Development (OECD) suggests that government initiatives worldwide that support high-technology industries involve significant resources and are focused increasingly on what policy makers consider strategic industries.[2] Pressure to limit public expenditure, comply with international codes (such as those of the World Trade Organization) or regional arrangements (such as the European Union subsidy codes) and the recognition of the risks of open-ended commitments to firms in rapidly evolving markets have led policy makers to focus more attention on the contributions of public-private partnerships.[3] In the past decade countries ranging from Japan to Finland to Germany have launched accelerated cooperative programs to restore or gain national competitiveness in key industries.

EXAMPLES OF INITIATIVES IN OTHER COUNTRIES

Cooperative activities are by no means confined to traditional competitors in high-technology industry. Finland has a general program of technology development called Tekes, which brings together key elements of Finnish technology strategy under a single organization. Parts of Finland's program have substantial similarities with the ATP. Reflecting the Finnish commitment to investments in new technologies, the Tekes program is funded at a similar level to the ATP. In 2001, Finland, a country of 5.1 million people, funded 2,261 research and development projects through Tekes with a total value of €387 million as compared with the approximately U.S.$146 million appropriated to the ATP in FY2001.[4]

Taiwan is another example of a nation committed to a broad-based effort to support high-technology sectors. Government policies in Taiwan have not only pursued capital market reform to create appropriate equity incentives for the growth of high technology but have also contributed substantial support through the ITRI (Industrial Technology Research Institute) established in 1974, and its main R&D facility ERSO (Electronics Research and Service Organization), which is focused on semiconductors. ERSO, originally supported by government funds, has since maintained itself by acquiring contracts. Taiwan further boosted its semiconductor industry by contributing public finds to the formation of UMC (United Microelectronics Corporation) in 1980, as well as initiating funding (with a more than 40 percent stake) for TSMC (Taiwan Semiconductor Manufacturing Company) in 1987. As part of a direct focus on a segment of high-technology

---

[2]See Brown, *op. cit.*

[3]The OECD, for example, has undertaken valuable work in this area, reflecting the interest of its membership.

[4]See the Tekes Web site, <http://www.tekes.fi/eng/information/stat00.html> (March 2001). Around €230 million of this funding, in the form of grants and loans, was aimed at company research and development projects, and about €140 million was aimed at university and research institution projects.

development, Taiwan established the Hsinchu Science Park in the mid-1970s, and it began operating in 1980 directly under the federal government's National Science Council; the park is now the core of Taiwan's integrated circuit (IC) industry. Hsinchu park has been credited with incubating most of Taiwan's IC factories—the bulk of which reside today either in the park itself or nearby. The park employed 83,000 people in 1999—an increase of more than four times from the 19,000 employed there in 1989.[5] Together, these policies have had a highly positive impact on the development of high-technology industry, especially semiconductors, in Taiwan.

NATIONAL AND REGIONAL PROGRAMS TO SUPPORT THE SEMICONDUCTOR INDUSTRY

The conviction that high-technology industries are fundamental to technological competency, national autonomy, economic growth, and high-wage, high-value-added employment is widespread among the major trading partners of the United States.[6] Nowhere is this more apparent than in the semiconductor industry. Consequently, many governments have adopted policies to support nationally based firms in the hope of capturing the benefits of this industry such as higher wage jobs, increased competitiveness, and future government revenue. Semiconductors are, and have been, the target of national policy, in both the United States and abroad. As Laura Tyson noted in her 1992 study:

> The semiconductor industry has never been free of the visible hand of government intervention. Competitive advantage in production and trade has been heavily influenced by policy choices, particularly in the United States and Japan. Some of these choices, such as the provision of public support for basic science, R&D, and education in the United States, have had general, not industry-specific objectives. But other choices, such as the provision of secured demand for industry output through military procurement in the United States and through preferential procurement of computers and telecommunications equipment in Japan, have been industry specific in intent and implementation.[7]

---

[5]For current programs in semiconductors, see National Research Council, *Securing the Future: Regional and National Programs to Support the Semiconductor Industry, op. cit.* Specifically, see the presentation made by Chien-Yuan Lin of Taiwan University in the Proceedings section of the report. For a well-researched overview of the many national programs in the same volume, see Thomas Howell, "Competing Programs: Government Support for Microelectronics."

[6]For a discussion of the importance of high-technology industries to national economies and the measures some countries adopt to capture these benefits, see National Research Council, *Conflict and Cooperation in National Competition for High-Technology Industry*, National Academy Press, Washington, D.C., 1996, especially box on pp. 33-35.

[7]*Laura D'Andrea Tyson, Who's Bashing Whom?: Trade Conflict in High Technology Industries.* Institute for International Economics, Washington, D.C., 1992, p. 85. For a review of government programs designed to develop and support the technologies underpinning the semiconductor industry, see Thomas Howell, "Competing Programs: Government Support for Microelectronics," *op. cit.*

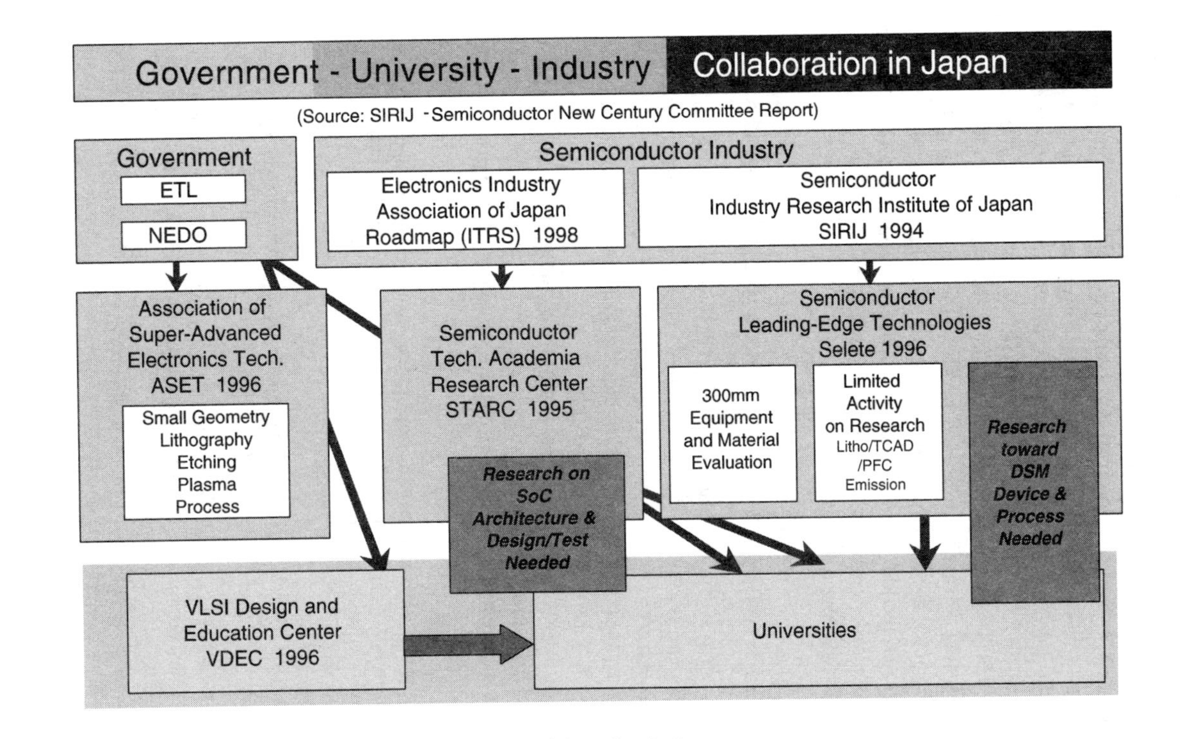

FIGURE 6 Government-university-industry collaboration in Japan.

As Tyson notes, the U.S. government provided early procurement-based funding to promote the development of semiconductors for both military and space exploration programs.[8] Also, as noted earlier, the United States undertook a series of initiatives in the 1980s to help redress the competitive position of the U.S. semiconductor industry. Notwithstanding the success of these policies—or because of them—the U.S. government's subsequent role in assisting the commercial semiconductor sector has been more restrained.[9] As a result, the United States presently has no comparable matrix of programs to support the semiconductor industry.[10] This fall-off in R&D support is not confined to semiconductors. The United States has also reduced the scale of its R&D investment in computers and computer architecture, in both absolute and relative terms.[11] The explanation for these reductions is complex, but these U.S. reductions do run contrary to global trends. The lag effects of what have been described as "random disinvestments" may compromise the U.S. government's ability to achieve other societal goals over the long term.

EXPANDING NATIONAL PROGRAMS ABROAD

By contrast, governments abroad remain active in supporting their respective semiconductor industries, as Box I indicates. Many governments have adopted policies to launch, revive, or restore their industries. If current policies remain in place, governments abroad will continue to intervene to support high-technology industries using a variety of mechanisms.

In spite of the recent pronounced downturn in the global semiconductor market, many governments remain active in their support of initiatives to promote the development of advanced microelectronics technology, often providing substan-

---

[8]Government procurement enabled U.S. firms to improve yield and efficiency through volume production and encouraged wider application of integrated circuit technology, first in military and then in commercial technologies. National Bureau of Standards, *The Influence of Defense Procurement and Sponsorship of Research and Development on the Development of the Civilian Electronics Industry*, June 30, 1977.

[9]See the paper by Thomas Howell, "Competing Programs: Government Support for Microelectronics," in *Securing the Future: Regional and National Programs to Support the Semiconductor Industry, op. cit.*

[10]The United States has greatly increased its research expenditures in biomedicine, but as described above, capitalizing on these investments will require complementary funding for other disciplines and related information technologies.

[11]In a recent report for this study, Kenneth Flamm documents this downturn. He notes that this downturn "would not be a source of concern if we were convinced that computing technology had matured" (i.e., that it was no longer an area with a high social payoff for the U.S. economy). Yet the contrary is the case. Given the potential for high-performance computing as a complement to technical advance in other high payoff areas, like biotechnology, Flamm suggests that it would be prudent for the United States "to plant more seed corn in this particular field." Kenneth Flamm, "The Federal Partnership with U.S. Industry in U.S. Computer Research: History and Recent Concerns" in National Research Council, *Capitalizing on New Needs and New Opportunities: Government-Industry Partnerships in Biotechnology and Information Technologies, op. cit.*, p. 220.

tial incentives to national industries to add manufacturing capacity. Some nations are also providing substantial incentive to attract native born and foreign talent to their national industry, in order to meet what some see as an emerging zero-sum competition for skilled labor.[12] In doing so, some national programs are altering the terms of global economic competition, with policies that differ in important ways from those of the traditional leaders.[13]

The levels of investment and promotional activity across many countries attest to the importance governments attach to the semiconductor industry. The emergence of China, for reasons of scale and skill, is likely to pose a major competitive challenge, especially as cooperation increases with the highly competent Taiwanese industry. At present China does not account for even one percent of the world semiconductor market, but much new capacity is scheduled to come on-stream.[14] In Shanghai, for example, two new fabrication plants ("fabs") are under construction, another two are on the drawing board, and over a dozen more are in the early planning stages.

Elsewhere in Asia, Taiwanese planners in mid-2000 envisioned that a total of 21 new 300mm fabs and 9 new 200mm fabs would be built by the year 2010. The government of Singapore has publicly set a goal of 20 fabs by the year 2005. In South Korea, the government pressured commercial banks to finance the move into chip making by the country's family-controlled conglomerates.[15] Malaysia has opened a $1.7 billion wafer fab and has planned to construct two more.[16] Japan, still a major player, is making a vigorous attempt to bring about a "national revival" in microelectronics, by emulating U.S. programs.[17]

---

[12]Thomas Howell, "Competing Programs: Government Support for Microelectronics," *op. cit.*

[13]As Thomas Howell documents through his extensive field research, there is now a broad area of well-funded programs to support national and regional semiconductor industries, as well as the international cooperation increasingly required in this global industry. See Thomas Howell, "Competing Programs: Government Support for Microelectronics," *op. cit.* For example, state-supported producers in Korea, Taiwan, Malaysia, and now China present special challenges in the competition for global markets in high-technology products. The 1996 STEP report identified this trend and predicted that it would accelerate. It has. See National Research Council, *Conflict and Cooperation in National Competition for High-Technology Industry*, National Academy Press, Washington, D.C., 1996, p. 21.

[14]"Is China's Semiconductor Industry Market Worth the Risk for Multinationals? Definitely!" *Cahners In-Stat Group* (March 29, 1999). According to the World Fab Watch (WFW) database, which is prepared by Strategic Marketing Associates and contains information on over one thousand fabs worldwide, as of this writing, there is a possibility of 84 fabs being constructed for integrated circuit fabrication between 2002 and 2005. This includes production, pilot, and R&D fabs. Of the total, twelve fabs are currently expected to be located in China. Strategic Marketing Associates, *World Fab Watch*, Santa Cruz, CA, 2002.

[15]See Thomas Howell, "Competing Programs: Government Support for Microelectronics," *op. cit.* Howell's figures and many of his conclusions are based primarily on personal interviews with industry officials in Asia. This type of field research on national policies for an industry is exceedingly rare in the U.S.

[16]"The Great Chip Glut," *The Economist,* August 11, 2001, <http://www.economistgroup.com>.

[17]See the presentations of Masataka Hirose, Toshiaki Masuhara, and Hideo Setoya in the Proceedings of National Research Council, *Securing the Future: Regional and National Programs to Support the Semiconductor Industry, op. cit.*

BOX I. National Programs to Support the Semiconductor Industry

Many nations are actively and substantially supporting initiatives in their respective national semiconductor industries. Some of these programs are listed below: [18]

Country	Project	Period of Project	Level of Funding	Purpose
Japan	Next Generation Semiconductor R&D Center (Super clean room)	2001-08	$300 million ($60 million in 2001)[19]	Process and device technology for 70 mm generation
Japan	Future Information Society Creation Laboratory	2001-06	$300 million	Create small-scale, very short-term semiconductor production line
Japan	ASET	1995-	$500 million	Lithography, semiconductor manufacturing technology
Japan	Nanotechnology Programs	1985-	$350 million in FY2001; METI labs conducting R&D	Basic R&D nanotechnology, includes microelectronics themes
Japan	Selete[20]	1996-	[21]	Manufacturing technology for 300-mm wafers
Taiwan	ASTRO	2000-	Government will fund half	Technology induction, upgrading of local industry
European Union	MEDEA	1997-2000	$720 million (est.)	Process technology, design, applications
European	MEDEA Plus	2001-09	$1,350 million (est.)	Systems-on-a-chip, UV lithography Union

Germany	Semiconductor 300	1996 -2000	$680 million	300 mm wafer technology
France	Crolles I and II	1998-	$136 million (est.)[22]	Pilot 300 mm fab
United States	MARCO	1997-	$75 million over 6 years	Basic microelectronics R&D
United States	National Nanotechnology Initiative	2000-	$270 million in 2000	Basic R&D on nanotechnology; includes same microelectronics themes
United States	DARPA	Permanent	$192 million in 2000 for "advanced electronics" technology"	Advanced lithography; nanomechnisms; electronic modules
United States[a]	SEMATECH	1989-1996	$850 million	Cooperative research facility to bench mark next-generation development of processes, products and tools; forum for information exchange and coordination of research projects.
United States	EUVL (Extreme Ultraviolet Lithography) CRADA[23]	1997-	$250 million	Advanced Lithography

[a] International SEMATECH, as its name suggests, involves companies from many countries and does not receive direct U.S. government support.

[18]See Thomas R. Howell, "Competing Programs: Government Support for Microelectronics," op. cit.

[19]METI requested $60 million in FY2001 budget for first year of a 7-year project

[20]Samsung is also a member of Selete.

[21]Privately funded but received NEDO contract to develop technology to cut PFC use.

[22]Crolles I reportedly received support of FF 900 million to FF 1 billion. Additional funds have been requested for Crolles II.

[23]The EUVL CRADA is in fact an international effort.

This summary of these national programs should not be interpreted as a criticism of them. The collective impact of these programs should help the semiconductor industry as a whole meet its increasingly complex technical challenges. At the same time, underlying these programs are genuine differences in national attitudes concerning a nation's knowledge and technology base. Notably, some nations believe the development of a nation's manufacturing capacity in leading industries to be an appropriate national goal worthy of sustained support.[24] In the case of both Europe and Japan, industry leaders are identifying what they see as the main semiconductor growth markets of the 21st century—wireless, wired telecommunications, and digital home appliances. U.S. companies have dominated computer applications of semiconductors, and in particular, personal computers, whose growth prospects may prove to be more limited in the future.[25]

COMPETITION AND COOPERATION

Competition and cooperation both transcend borders. In the realm of high technology, competition and cooperation are often the two faces of a coin. While competition for high-technology industry is not new, it does seem to be accelerating, as new entrants put in more resources, often in new or expanded organizations.[26] Some advocates of free global trade argue against these programs; yet preaching that these activities of trading partners constitute unwarranted intervention in the market ignores the origins of many U.S. industries, the interventionist tradition of the countries concerned, and the frequent success of these programs. Add to that the fact that exhortations have little effect in international economic relations, especially when nations believe their economic future is at stake. The situation is further complicated by the widespread belief in the need for governments to support many fledgling technologies—although the terms and nature of this aid vary greatly across countries.

At the same time, in many industries international cooperation is increasingly required to address the cost, complexity, and risk of new generations of

---

[24]Some nations pursue consumer welfare as an implicit, if vaguely defined, goal, while other nations adopt explicit national economic strategies, designed to pursue national economic strength through the acquisition of the capability to manufacture high-technology products. See National Research Council, *Conflict and Cooperation in National Competition for High-technology Industry, op. cit.*, pp. 12-27 and pp. 51-54. See also Richard Samuel's *Rich Nation, Strong Army: National Security and Technological Transformation of Japan*, Ithaca, NY: Cornell University Press, 1994.

[25]"From Stagnation to Growth, The Push to Strengthen Design," *Nikkei Microdevices* (January 2001); "Three Major European LSI Makers Show Stable Growth Through Large Investments," *Nikkei Microdevices* (January 2001). See also, Thomas Howell, "Competing Programs: Government Support for Microelectronics," *op. cit.*

[26]For a discussion of national programs to encourage high-technology industry and to capture their benefits for national economies, see National Research Council, *Conflict and Cooperation,* 1996, *op. cit.* For a comprehensive review of national programs for semiconductors, see Thomas Howell, *op. cit.*

Box J. International SEMATECH

Begun in 1995 to develop common technology for next generation of 300-mm wafers, SEMATECH evolved in 1999 into full international cooperation in non-competitive semiconductor manufacturing technology.[27] International SEMATECH is today the world's largest semiconductor research consortium. Member companies from the United States, Asia, and Europe are cooperating in key areas of semiconductor technology, sharing expenses and risk. It is important to note that the Japanese producers, with one Korean member, Samsung, have mounted a major but separate consortium called SELETE. Their common aim is to accelerate development of the advanced manufacturing technologies required to build the more powerful semiconductors necessary to sustain the exceptional growth of this industry.[28]

technologies. The vigorous competition for the benefits of high-technology industry is thus both complicated and complemented by the frequent need for cooperation to achieve common goals.

A cooperative approach to science and technology development is thus one of the hallmarks of the late twentieth century. Cooperation across national frontiers is expanding, aided by new communications technologies and motivated by the global nature of many scientific challenges. Within and among nations, cooperation between governments and industry is expanding to meet national goals and common technological challenges. Strategic alliances among businesses are also expanding dramatically, enabling firms to meet a variety of goals from shar-

[27]The internationalization of SEMATECH, though it occurred after the end of U.S. government funding, was not without controversy. In the context of international trade, cooperation and competition are often the two sides of the same coin; the judgment to internationalize SEMATECH appears to have rested on the belief that cooperation in this instance would best serve the U.S. industry's interests. See Thomas Howell, "Competing Programs, Government Support for Microelectronics," in National Research Council, *Securing the Future: Regional and National Programs to Support the Semiconductor Industry, op. cit.,* for a discussion of cooperative programs. For a discussion of the cooperative and competitive elements in such programs, see National Research Council, *Conflict and Cooperation in National Competition for High-Technology Industry, op. cit.*

[28]International SEMATECH addresses areas essential to the continued progress of semiconductor science, including lithography, interconnect, front-end processes, advanced technology, manufacturing methods, and environment, safety, and health. International SEMATECH also provides important resources to the semiconductor industry, including coordinating global standards for 300-mm manufacturing; enhancing relationships between manufacturers and tool suppliers; and developing application-focused statistical training for the industry. For additional information on International SEMATECH, see <http://www.sematech.org/>.

ing expertise and costs to establishing global standards and assuring market access for final products. The global nature of many technological challenges and the enormous expense associated with developing new technologies has made international cooperation an essential element of national science and technology policy.

Successful cooperation, both among nations and among firms, requires care and commitment. Care is necessary because much depends on the choice of partner and the clear articulation of goals and responsibilities. The sustained commitment of individuals and effective organizations combined with sustained funding are essential for cooperative activities to bear fruit. To fully realize the benefits of international collaboration, substantial vision and commitment are required of researchers and policy makers alike.

The Committee has sought to foster such cooperation across international borders among researchers and policy makers. At the request of the White House, the State Department, and the European Union, the Academies Committee organized in June 1998 a major two-day conference, convened at the National Academies, to celebrate the signature of the 1997 Agreement for Scientific and Technological Cooperation between the European Community and the Government of the United States of America and to inform the U.S. and European research communities of its relevance. While the agreement itself represents a significant achievement, creating a bridge between the R&D systems on both sides of the Atlantic, its full potential can be realized only if it can encourage mutually beneficial cooperation.[29]

The conference served as an important opportunity to publicize the agreement within the research community and among policy makers on both sides of the Atlantic. By bringing together experts in substantive areas where opportunities for mutually beneficial partnerships were believed to exist, the conference was able to examine crosscutting issues of common interest in such areas as the framework for R&D cooperation, small business development, and the internationalization of the technical workforce. As intended, the conference identified technology areas of interest to the United States and our European partners, helped to clarify the modalities of U.S.-E.U. cooperation, and furthered mutually beneficial science and technology cooperation between the European Union and the United States—two of the premier research areas of the world.

[29]See National Research Council, *New Vistas in Transatlantic Science and Technology Cooperation*, C. Wessner, ed., Washington, D.C.: National Academy Press, 1999.

VIII

CONCLUSIONS

Conclusions

The analysis of Government-Industry Partnerships for the Development of New Technologies project has focused on the contributions that partnerships can make by accelerating the development of new technologies. The 18 public meetings and 10 major reports produced in the course of this analysis represent a substantial contribution to our understanding of the operation of partnerships.[1] The Committee's desire to carry out an analysis of current partnerships that is directly relevant to contemporary policy making has conditioned the selection of the specific programs reviewed. This summary of the overall study identifies several key lessons that are important to the development of new technologies in the United States.

KEY LESSONS

Partnerships work. To be effective, partnerships need to be properly constructed and ably led. They work best with clear goals, shared contributions, and regular evaluations. Well-structured and -operated partnerships serve as valuable intermediate organizations able to bring together the partners needed to develop new products and processes of value to society as a whole. Innovation in the United States has often been accelerated through public support for research and development partnerships. Federal participation in the innovation process, which

[1]It is important to acknowledge at the same time that the Committee's analysis is a necessarily limited portion of the variety of cooperative activity that takes place between the government and the private sector.

extends back to the beginning of the republic, has been characterized by experimentation and flexibility. These attributes contribute to the versatility and vigor of the U.S. innovation system.

- **Partnerships Involve Success *and* Failure**
  Partnerships are essentially experiments; each new effort entails genuine risk as well as the potential of societal gains. With experimentation comes failure as well as success. In assessing the outcomes of these partnership experiments, it is important to recognize that the failure of a particular project is not necessarily an indication of an overall program failure; failure is to be expected if genuinely risky ventures are undertaken. A willingness to encourage experiments in public-private cooperation, however, must also be matched by a willingness to identify and cancel projects that fail, or simply under-perform.

- **Strength Through Diversity**
  The U.S. innovation system draws strength from the variety of its mission priorities and institutions. The array of objectives, organizations, and partnership mechanisms reflect the range of challenges faced by government agencies charged with complex missions, industries facing new technological challenges, and universities increasingly seeking to move promising ideas from the laboratory to the marketplace.

- **Sustained Support**
  Maintaining the strength of this innovation system requires substantial and sustained federal R&D support. Furthermore, federal R&D investments are needed across a broad portfolio of research and development activities, both because new technologies emerge over time and because advances in one sector can have a profound impact on progress in other sectors.

- **Multidisciplinary Approaches**
  New research opportunities, such as those emerging from the genome, increasingly require cross-disciplinary approaches. Greater support and facilitation for interdisciplinary training and multidisciplinary research is essential therefore to promote new frontiers in technology. Partnerships are a key mechanism to facilitate cross-disciplinary cooperation.

- **Linkages**
  More broadly, partnerships also serve to link different parts of the U.S. innovation system. These include firms of different sizes and specialties, universities in different regions, and the exceptional facilities of the national laboratories. In doing so, public-private partnerships help achieve a

creative balance between diversity and coordination, while helping to bring research from development to application.

PARTNERSHIPS AND EARLY-STAGE FINANCE

Early-stage financing of innovation plays a key role in supporting the development of new technologies and is therefore a focus of innovation policy. Award partnerships, such as those in the ATP and SBIR programs, can provide an effective means to encourage small firms with promising ideas and technologies to gain access to early-stage financing. In doing so, partnerships contribute to the achievement of government missions in important ways.

Programs such as the SBIR can accelerate and facilitate the modernization of the U.S. defense establishment by introducing new and better information systems. Programs such as the ATP are helping to bring new energy-saving technologies to the market as well as new medical devices and instruments to the healthcare system. Around the world award-based partnerships, such as the ATP and SBIR, are increasingly seen as an effective means to overcome obstacles to new technological development.

Inadequate access to early-stage finance can pose no less a barrier to advocates of new ideas in large firms than for small firm entrepreneurs. Partnership awards and participation in consortium with universities and small firms can help provide incentives to researchers and managers in larger firms to push new "game changing" technologies. Large firms in collaboration with small firms can often make partnerships more effective by drawing on the technical expertise; the financial, engineering, and management resources; and the marketing skills marshaled by large firms. Both large and small firms can benefit from partnerships, and the society as a whole can benefit from their joint accomplishments.

U.S. PARTNERSHIPS IN A GLOBAL CONTEXT

The public discussion, empirical research, and well-documented analysis of U.S. programs have generated substantial interest among policy makers in the United States. There is also growing interest in the contributions of partnerships among foreign policy makers, research institutes, and leading international organizations such as the Organisation for Economic Cooperation and Development. This interest reflects the awareness of the benefits of science-based growth and the belief in the need for effective public-private cooperation to help achieve this objective.

In the global economy, technology development has important international dimensions. Initiatives in international benchmarking of national and regional technology programs are therefore important. Such analysis helps us learn about what other participants in the global economy believe is necessary and effective. Cooperative comparison allows for exchanges of experience, research, and sometimes solutions to issues and questions common to many technology programs. Cooperation among firms and facilitative agreements among governments can help to further the progress of innovation. The emphasis on this international dimension reflects the twin realities of global competition and cooperation.

Effective public-private partnerships can help industry to bring the benefits of science and technology to society. Technologies concerned with medical diagnostics, for example, offer the means for improving the quality and length of our lives. Collectively these technologies offer vast personal and societal benefits—whether through more effective diagnostic tools and medical treatments or new information technology contributions to increased labor productivity.

POLICY IMPACTS OF THIS STUDY OF PARTNERSHIPS

The analyses and results presented throughout this study of government-industry partnerships have, as intended, already resulted in concrete policy actions. The enhancement of the U.S.-E.U. science and technology cooperation, the decision of the Department of Defense to continue and expand the Fast Track component of the SBIR program, the adoption of many of the study's recommendations and findings on the ATP program, and the passage of legislation supporting a solid-state lighting consortium, all speak to the direct policy impact of the committee's research and analysis.

The Committee has also highlighted pressing needs in the U.S. R&D portfolio by recommending increased support for research in the academic disciplines supporting continued advances in new technologies. While this summary report underscores the policy relevance and impact of public-private partnerships in the United States, it also suggests the need for continued, pragmatic assessment of the conditions under which public-private partnerships can best contribute to U.S. technological leadership, economic growth, and national security.

Finally, partnerships, flexible in form and scale, are an effective policy tool to rapidly respond to new national security needs. In the current war on terrorism partnerships can be an effective means to channel the nation's deep but often scattered reservoirs of expertise and innovative potential to develop capacities to anticipate, counter, and cope with this menace.

IX

BIBLIOGRAPHY

Bibliography

Acs, Zoltan J. and David B. Audretsch. 1991. *Innovation and Small Firms.* Cambridge, MA: MIT Press.

Adams, Chris. 2001. "Laboratory Hybrids: How Adroit Scientists Aid Biotech Companies with Taxpayer Money—NIH Grants Go to Non-profits Tied to For-profit Firms set up by Researchers," *Wall Street Journal.* New York: Dow Jones and Company. January 30. p. A1.

Ambrose, Stephen. 2000. *Nothing Like It in the World: The Men Who Built the Transcontinental Railroad 1863-1869.* New York: Simon and Schuster.

American Association for the Advancement of Science. 2002. *AAAS Preliminary Analysis of R&D in FY 2003 Budget.* February 8. <www.aaas.org/spp/R&D>.

Audretsch, David B. 1995. *Innovation and Industry Evolution.* Cambridge, MA: The MIT Press.

Audretsch, David B., Barry Bozeman, Kathryn L. Combs, Maryann Feldman, Albert N. Link, Donald S. Siegel, Paula Stephan, Gregory Tassey, and Charles Wessner. 2002. "The Economics of Science and Technology." *Journal of Technology Transfer.* 27: 155-203.

Audretsch, David B. and Roy Thurik. 1999. *Innovation, Industry, Evolution, and Employment.* Cambridge, UK: Cambridge University Press.

Baily, M. N. and A. Chakrabati. 1998. *Innovation and the Productivity Crisis.* Washington, D.C.: Brookings.

Baily, M.N. and R.Z. Lawrence. 2001. "Do We Have an E-conomy?" NBER Working Paper 8243. April 23.

Bilstein, Roger E. 1989. *A History of the NACA and NASA, 1915-1990.* Washington, D.C.: National Aeronautics and Space Administration.

Bingham, Richard. 1998. *Industrial Policy American Style: From Hamilton to HDTV.* New York: M.E. Sharpe.

Borrus, Michael. 1997. Testimony before the U.S. House of Representatives Committee on Science: Subcommittee on Technology. April 10.

Borrus, Michael and Jay Stowsky. 1997. "Technology Policy and Economic Growth." BRIE Working Paper 97. April.

Brander, J.A. and B.J. Spencer. 1983. "International R&D Rivalry and Industrial Strategy." *Review of Economic Studies.* 50:707-722.

Brander, J.A. and B.J. Spencer, 1985. "Export Subsidies and International Market Share Rivalry." *Journal of International Economics*. 16:83-100.

Branscomb, L. 2001. Testimony before U.S. House of Representatives Committee on Science: Subcommittee on Technology. June 14.

Branscomb, L. and P. Auerswald. 2001. *Taking Technical Risk: How Innovators, Executives, and Investors Manage High-Tech Risks.* Cambridge, MA: The MIT Press.

Branscomb, L. M. and J. Keller, eds. 1998. *Investing in Innovation: Creating a Research and Innovation Policy.* Cambridge, MA: MIT Press.

Brown, George and James Turner. 1999. "The Federal Role in Small Business Research." *Issues in Science and Technology.* Summer. p. 52.

Brown, Martin. 1995. *Impacts of National Technology Programs.* Paris: Organisation for Economic Co-operation and Development.

Browning, L. D., J. M. Beyer, & J. C. Shetler. 1995. "Building Cooperation in a Competitive Industry: SEMATECH and the semiconductor industry." *Academy of Management Journal.* 38(1): 113-151.

Browning, Larry D. and Judy C. Shetler. 2000. *SEMATECH: Saving the U.S. Semiconductor Industry.* College Station: Texas A&M University Press.

Cahners In-Stat Group. 1999. "Is China's Semiconductor Industry Market Worth the Risk for Multinationals? Definitely!" Cahners In-Stat Group. March 29.

Campbell, Donald E. 1995. *Incentives: Motivations and the Economics of Information.* Cambridge, UK: Cambridge University Press.

Chandler, Alfred P. 1962. *Strategy and Structure: Chapters in History of the Industrial Enterprise.* Cambridge, MA: MIT Press.

Chesbrough, Hank. 2001. "Is the Central R&D Lab Obsolete?" *Technology Review.* April 24.

Coburn, Christopher and Dan Berglund. 1995. *Partnerships: A Compendium of State and Federal Cooperative Technology Programs.* Columbus, OH: Battelle Press.

Cohen , Linda R. and Roger G. Noll. 1991. *The Technology Pork Barrel.* Washington, D.C.: The Brookings Institution.

Council of Economic Advisors. 1995. *Economic Report of the President.* Washington, D.C.: U.S. Government Printing Office. January.

Council of Economic Advisers. 1995. *Supporting Research and Development to Promote Economic Growth: The Federal Government's Role.* Washington, D.C.: U.S. Government Printing Office.

Council of Economic Advisors. 2000. *The Annual Report of the Council of Economic Advisors.* Washington, D.C.: U.S. Government Printing Office.

Council of Economic Advisors. 2001. *Economic Report of the President.* Washington, D.C.: U.S. Government Printing Office. January.

Council of Economic Advisors. 2002. *Economic Report of the President.* Washington, D.C.: U.S. Government Printing Office. January.

David, Paul. 2000. "Understanding Digital Technology's Evolution and the Path of Measured Productivity Growth: Present and Future in the Mirror of the Past." in E. Brynjolfsson and Brian Kahin, eds. *Understanding the Digital Economy: Data, Tools, and Research.* Cambridge, MA: MIT Press.

David, Paul A., Bronwyn H. Hall, and Andrew A. Toole. 1999. "Is Public R&D a Complement or Substitute for Private R&D? A Review of the Econometric Evidence." NBER Working Paper 7373, October.

Davis, Steven J., John Haltiwanger, and Scott Schuh. 1994. "Small Business and Job Creation: Dissecting the Myth and Reassessing the Facts." *Business Economics.* 29(3):113-22.

de Tocqueville, Alexis. 2000. *Democracy in America.* Chicago: University of Chicago Press.

Diebold, Jr., William. 1980. "Past and Future Industrial Policy in the United States." In J. Pinder, ed., *National Industrial Strategies and the World Economy.* London: Allanheld, Osmun & Company.

The Economist. 1989. "The Rise and Fall of America's Small Firms." *The Economist.* January 21. pp. 73-74.

The Economist. 2000. "A Thinker's Guide" *The Economist.* March 30.

The Economist. 2001. "The Great Chip Glut." *The Economist.* August 11.

The Economist. 2001. "Protein Based Computer Memories, Data Harvest." *The Economist.* December 22.

Evanson, Robert E. and Wallace E. Huffman. 1993. *Science for Agriculture: A Long-term Perspective.* Ames: Iowa State University Press.

Fallows, J. 1994. *Looking into the Sun: The Rise of the New East Asian Economic and Political System.* New York: Pantheon Books.

Flamm, Kenneth. 1988. *Creating the Computer.* Washington, D.C.: Brookings.

Flamm, Kenneth. 1996. *Mismanaged Trade? Strategic Policy and the Semiconductor Industry.* Washington, D.C.: Brookings.

Fogel, Robert W. 1964. *Railroads and American Economic Growth: Essays in Econometric History.* Baltimore: Johns Hopkins University Press.

Galbraith, John Kenneth. 1957. *The New Industrial State.* Boston: Houghton Mifflin.

Graham, Otis L. 1992. *Losing Time: The Industrial Policy Debate.* Cambridge, MA: Harvard University.

Greenspan, Alan. 2000. Remarks before the *White House Conference on the New Economy.* Washington, D.C. April 5.

Griliches, Zvi. 1990. *The Search for R&D Spillovers.* Cambridge, MA: Harvard University Press.

Grindley, Peter, David C Mowery, and Brian Silverman. 1994. "SEMATECH and Collaborative Research: Lessons in the Design of High-Technology Consortia." *Journal of Policy Analysis and Management.* 13(4):723-58.

Grossman, Gene and Elhanan Helpman. 1993. *Innovation and Growth in the Global Economy.* Cambridge, MA: MIT Press.

Hart, David M. 1998. *Forged Consensus: Science, Technology, and Economic Policy in the United States, 1921-1953.* Princeton: Princeton University Press.

Horrigan, John B. 1999. "Cooperating Competitors: A Comparison of MCC and SEMATECH." Monograph. Washington, D.C.: National Research Council.

Hounshell, David A. 1985. *From the American System to Mass Production, 1800-1932.* Baltimore: Johns Hopkins University Press.

Hudgins, Edward L. 1995. Testimony before the Senate Committee on Commerce, Science, and Transportation. August 1.

International SEMATECH. 2002. *Annual Report 2001.* Austin: International SEMATECH.

Jarboe, Kenan Patrick and Robert D. Atkinson. 1998. *The Case for Technology in the Knowledge Economy; R&D, Economic Growth and the Role of Government.* Washington, D.C.: Progressive Policy Institute. June 1.

Johnson, Chalmers. 1982. *MITI and the Japanese Miracle: The Growth of Industrial Policy 1925-1975.* Stanford, CA: Stanford University Press.

Jorgenson, Dale and Kevin Stiroh. 2000. "Raising the Speed Limit: U.S. Economic Growth in the Information Age." *Brookings Papers-on-Economic-Activity.* Washington, D.C.: Brookings. pp. 125-211.

Kenney, Martin, ed. 2000. *Understanding Silicon Valley: The Anatomy of an Entrepreneurial Region.* Stanford: Stanford University Press.

Kleinman, Daniel Lee. 1995. *Politics on the Endless Frontier: Postwar Research Policy in the United States.* Durham, N.C.: Duke University Press.

Koizumi, Kei and Paul W. Turner. 2002. *Congressional Action on Research and Development in the FY 2002 Budget.* Washington, D.C.: American Association for the Advancement of Science.

Kornai, Janos. 1980. *Economics of Shortage.* Amsterdam: North Holland.

Krugman, P. Undated. "Some Chaotic Thoughts on Regional Dynamics." at <http://www.wws.princeton.edu/~pkrugman/temin.html>.

Krugman, P. 1990. *Rethinking International Trade.* Cambridge, MA: MIT Press.

Krugman, P. 1991. *Geography and Trade,* Cambridge, MA: MIT Press.

Krugman, P. 1994. *Peddling Prosperity: Economic Sense and Nonsense in an Age of Diminished Expectations*. New York: W.W. Norton Press.

Langlois, Richard N. 1991. "Schumpeter and the Obsolescence of the Entrepreneur." Working Paper 91-1503. University of Connecticut Department of Economics. November.

Langlois, Richard N. and Paul L. Robertson. 1996. "Stop Crying over Spilt Knowledge: A Critical Look at the Theory of Spillovers and Technical Change." Paper prepared for the MERIT Conference on Innovation, Evolution, and Technology. Maastricht, Netherlands. August 25-27.

Larson, Charles F. 2000. "The Boom in Industry Research." *Issues in Science and Technology*. Summer.

Lebow, Irwin. 1995. *Information Highways and Byways*. New York: Institute of Electrical and Electronics Engineers.

Linden, Greg, David Mowery, and Rosemarie Ziedonis. 2001. «National Technology Policy in Global Markets.» In Albert Link and Maryann Feldman, eds. *Innovation Policy in the Knowledge-based Economy*. Boston: Kluwer Academic Publishers.

Link, A. N. 1996. "Research Joint Ventures: Patterns from Federal Register Filings." *Review of Industrial Organization*. 11(5): 617-628.

Link, A. N. 1999. "Public/Private Partnerships as a Tool to Support Industrial R&D: Experiences in the United States." *Final Report to the Working Group on Innovation and Technology Policy of the OECD Committee for Scientific and Technology Policy*. January.

Luger, Michael I. and Harvey A. Goldstein. 1991. *Technology in the Garden; Research Parks & Regional Economic Development*. Chapel Hill: University of North Carolina Press.

Mann, Catherine. 1993. *Is the U.S. Trade Deficit Sustainable?* Washington, D.C.: Institute for International Economics.

Mann, Charles C. 2000. "The End of Moore's Law?" *Technology Review*. May/June.

Mansfield, Edwin. 1985. "How Fast Does New Industrial Technology Leak Out?" *Journal of Industrial Economics*. 34(2):217-224.

Mansfield, Edwin. 1991. "Academic Research and Industrial Innovation" *Research Policy*. February.

Marshall, Alfred. 1920. *Industry and Trade*. 3rd edition. London: Macmillan.

Martin, Brookes and Zaki Wahhaj. 2000. "The Shocking Economic Impact of B2B." *Global Economic Paper*. 37. Goldman Sachs. February 3.

May, John. 2002. "Angel Alliances and Angel Practices." Presented at The State of the Angel Market Workshop. Boston, MA. March 27.

McCraw, Thomas. 1986. "Mercantilism and the Market: Antecedents of American Industrial Policy." In *The Politics of Industrial Policy*. Claude E. Barfield and William A. Schambra, eds. Washington, D.C.: American Enterprise Institute for Public Policy Research.

McKinsey Global Institute. 2001. *U.S. Productivity Growth 1995-2000, Understanding the Contribution of Information Technology Relative to Other Factors*. Washington, D.C.: McKinsey & Company. October.

Merrill, Stephen A. and Michael McGeary. 1999. "Who's Balancing the Federal Research Portfolio and How?" *Science*. 285(September 10):1679-1680.

Middendorf, William H. 1981. *What Every Engineer Should Know About Inventing*. New York and Basel: Marcel Dekker Inc.

Moore, Gordon E. 1965. "Cramming More Components Onto Integrated Circuits." *Electronics*. 38(8) April 19.

Moore, Gordon E. 1997. "The Continuing Silicon Technology Evolution Inside the PC Platform." *Intel Developer Update*. Issue 2. October 15.

Mowery, David. 1998. "Collaborative R&D: How Effective Is It?" *Issues in Science and Technology*. 15(1):37.

Mowery, David and N. Hatch. 2002. "Managing the Development and Introduction of New Manufacturing Processes in the Global Semiconductor Industry." In G. Dosi, R. Nelson, and S. Winter, eds. *The Nature and Dynamics of Organizational Capabilities*. New York: Oxford University Press.

Mowery, David and Nathan Rosenberg. 1989. *Technology and the Pursuit of Economic Growth,* Cambridge: Cambridge University Press.

Mowery, David and Nathan Rosenberg. 1998. *Paths of Innovation: Technological Change in 20th Century America.* New York: Cambridge University Press.

Mowery, David and Brian Silverman. 1996. "SEMATECH and Collaborative Research: Lessons in the Design of High-Technology Consortia." *Journal of Policy Analysis and Management.* 13(4).

Nadiri, Ishaq. 1993. *Innovations and Technological Spillovers.* NBER Working Paper No. 4423.

Nance, Scott. 2000. "Broad Federal Research Required to Keep Semiconductors on Track." *New Technology Week.* October 30.

National Bureau of Standards. 1977. *The Influence of Defense Procurement and Sponsorship of Research and Development on the Development of the Civilian Electronics Industry.* National Bureau of Standards. June 30.

National Research Council. 1992. *The Government Role in Civilian Technology: Building a New Alliance.* Washington, D.C.: National Academy Press.

National Research Council. 1996. *Conflict and Cooperation in National Competition for High Technology Industry.* Washington, D.C.: National Academy Press.

National Research Council. 1999. *The Advanced Technology Program: Challenges and Opportunities.* Charles W. Wessner, ed. Washington, D.C.: National Academy Press.

National Research Council. 1999. *Funding a Revolution; Government Support for Computing Research.* Washington, D.C.: National Academy Press.

National Research Council. 1999. *Industry-Laboratory Partnerships: A Review of the Sandia Science and Technology Park Initiative.* Charles W. Wessner, ed. Washington, D.C.: National Academy Press.

National Research Council. 1999. *New Vistas in Transatlantic Science and Technology Cooperation.* Charles W. Wessner, ed. Washington, D.C.: National Academy Press.

National Research Council. 1999. *The Small Business Innovation Research Program: Challenges and Opportunities.* Charles W. Wessner, ed. Washington, D.C.: National Academy Press.

National Research Council. 1999. *U.S. Industry in 2000: Studies in Competitive Performance.* Washington, D.C.: National Academy Press.

National Research Council. 2000. *The Small Business Innovation Research Program: An Assessment of the Department of Defense Fast Track Initiative.* Charles W. Wessner, ed. Washington, D.C.: National Academy Press.

National Research Council. 2001. *The Advanced Technology Program: Assessing Outcomes.* Charles W. Wessner, ed. Washington, D.C.: National Academy Press.

National Research Council. 2001. *A Review of the New Initiatives at the NASA Ames Research Center.* Charles W. Wessner, ed. Washington, D.C.: National Academy Press.

National Research Council. 2001. *Review of the Research Program of the Partnership for a New Generation of Vehicles: Seventh Report.* Washington, D.C.: National Academy Press.

National Research Council. 2001. *Trends in Federal Support of Research and Graduate Education.* Stephen A. Merrill, ed. Washington, D.C.: National Academy Press.

National Research Council. 2002. *Capitalizing on New Needs and New Opportunities: Government-Industry Partnerships in Biotechnology and Information Technologies.* Charles W. Wessner, ed. Washington, D.C.: National Academy Press.

National Research Council. 2002. *Making the Nation Safer: The Role of Science and Technology in Countering Terrorism.* Washington, D.C.: National Academy Press.

National Research Council. 2002. *Measuring and Sustaining the New Economy.* D. Jorgenson and C. Wessner, eds. Washington, D.C.: National Academy Press.

National Research Council. 2002. *Partnerships for Solid-State Lighting.* Charles W. Wessner, ed. Washington, D.C.: National Academy Press.

National Research Council. 2002. *Small Wonders, Endless Frontiers: A Review of the National Nanotechnology Initiative.* Washington, D.C.: National Academy Press.

National Research Council. Forthcoming. *Securing the Future: Regional and National Programs to Support the Semiconductor Industry.* Charles W. Wessner, ed. Washington, D.C.: National Academies Press.

National Science Board. 1998. *Science and Engineering Indicators, 1998.* Arlington, VA: National Science Foundation.

Nelson, Richard R. 1982. *Government and Technological Progress.* New York: Pergamon Press.

Nelson, Richard R. 1993. *National Innovation Systems.* New York: Oxford University Press.

Nelson, Richard R. 2000. *The Sources of Economic Growth.* Cambridge, MA: Harvard University Press.

Nikkei Microdevices. 2001. "From Stagnation to Growth, The Push to Strengthen Design." *Nikkei Microdevices.* January.

Nikkei Microdevices. 2001. "Three Major European LSI Makers Show Stable Growth Through Large Investments." *Nikkei Microdevices.* January.

Noll, Roger. 2002. "Federal R&D in the Anti-Terrorist Era." In *Innovation Policy and the Economy, Vol. 3.* Adam B. Jaffe, Joshua Lerner and Scott Stern, eds. Cambridge, MA: MIT Press.

North, Douglass C. 1990. *Institutions, Institutional Change, and Economic Performance.* Cambridge: Cambridge University Press.

Office of Science and Technology Policy. 2000. *Fact Sheet on How Federal R&D Investments Drive the U.S. Economy.* Washington, D.C.: Executive Office of the President. June 15.

Okimoto, Daniel I. 1989. *Between MITI and the Market: Japanese Industrial Policy for High Technology.* Stanford, California: Stanford University Press.

Oliner, Stephen and Daniel Sichel. 2000. "The Resurgence of Growth in the late 1990s: Is Information Technology the Story?" *Journal of Economic Perspectives* 14(4) Fall.

Olson, Mancur. 1965. *The Logic of Collective Action.* Cambridge, MA: Harvard University Press.

Organisation for Economic Co-operation and Development. 1997. *Small Business Job Creation and Growth: Facts, Obstacles, and Best Practices.* Paris: Organisation for Economic Co-operation and Development.

Organisation for Economic Co-operation and Development. 2000. *Is There a New Economy? A First Report on the OECD Growth Project.* Paris: Organisation for Economic Co-operation and Development. June.

Ostrom, Elinor. 1998. "A Behavioral Approach to the Rational Choice Theory of Collective Action." *American Political Science Review.* 92(1).

Ostrom, Vincent. 1991. *The Meaning of American Federalism: Constituting a Self-Governing Society.* San Francisco: Institute for Contemporary Studies Press.

Packan, Paul A. 1999. "Pushing the Limits: Integrated Circuits Run Into Limits Due to Transistors." *Science.* September 24.

Polanyi, Michael. 1951. *Logic of Liberty.* Chicago: University of Chicago Press.

Porter, Michael. 1998. "Clusters and the New Economics of Competition." *Harvard Business Review.* November – December.

Porter, Michael. 2001. *Clusters of Innovation: Regional Foundations of Competitiveness.* Washington, D.C.: Council on Competitiveness.

Prestowitz, Clyde. 1988. *Trading Places.* New York: Basic Books.

Rodgers, T.J. 1998. "Silicon Valley Versus Corporate Welfare." *CATO Institute Briefing Papers.* Briefing Paper No. 37. April 27.

Romer, Paul. 1990. "Endogenous Technological Change." *Journal of Political Economy.* 98(5):71-102.

Rosenberg, Nathan. 1982. *Inside the Black Box: Technology and Economics.* New York: Cambridge University Press.

Rosenbloom, Richard and William Spencer. 1996. *Engines of Innovation: U.S. Industrial Research at the End of an Era.* Boston: Harvard Business School Press.

Ruttan, Vernon W. 2001. *Technology, Growth and Development: An Induced Innovation Perspective.* New York: Cambridge University Press.

Samuel, Richard. 1994. *Rich Nation, Strong Army: National Security and Technological Transformation of Japan*. Ithaca, NY: Cornell University Press.

Saxenian, AnnaLee. 1994. *Regional Advantage: Culture and Competition in Silicon Valley and Route 128*. Cambridge, MA: Harvard University Press.

Schaller, Robert R. 1999. "Technology Roadmaps: Implications for Innovation, Strategy, and Policy." Ph.D. Dissertation Proposal, Institute for Public Policy, George Mason University.

Scherer, F.M. 1999. *New Perspectives on Economic Growth and Technological Innovation*. Washington, D.C.: Brookings.

Schumpeter, Joseph A. 1950. *Capitalism, Socialism and Democracy*. New York: Harper and Row.

Semiconductor Industry Association. 2001. *2001 Annual Databook: Review of Global and U.S. Semiconductor Competitive Trends, 1978-2000*. San Jose, CA: Semiconductor Industry Association.

Silber & Associates. 1996. *Survey of Advanced Technology Program 1990-1992 Awardees: Company Opinion about the ATP and its Early Effects*. NIST GCR 97-707. February.

Smith, Hedrick. 1995. *Rethinking America*. New York: Random House.

Sohl, Jeffrey E. 1999. "The Early-Stage Equity Market in the USA." *Venture Capital*. 1(2): 101-20.

Sohl, Jeffery E. 2002. "The Private Equity Market in the U.S.: What a Long Strange Trip It Has Been." Mimeo. University of New Hampshire: Whittemore School of Business and Economics.

Solomon Associates. 1993. *Advanced Technology Program: An Assessment of Short-Term Impacts—First Competition Participants*. Solomon Associates. February.

Solow, Robert S. 1957. "Technical Change and the Aggregate Production Function." *Review of Economics and Statistics*. 39: 312-320.

Sporck, Charles E. (with Richard L. Molay). 2001. *Spinoff: A Personal History of the Industry that Changed the World*. Sarnac Lake, New York: Sarnac Lake Publishing.

Strategic Marketing Associates. 2002. *World Fab Watch*. Santa Cruz, CA: World Fab Watch.

Stowsky, Jay. 1996. "Politics and Policy: The Technology Reinvestment Program and the Dilemmas of Dual Use." Mimeo. University of California.

Susaki, Hajime. 2000. "Japanese Semiconductor Industry's Competitiveness: LSI Industry in Jeopardy." *Nikkei Microdevices*. December.

Tennenhouse, David. 2002. Joint Strategic Assessments Group and Defense Advanced Research Projects Agency conference, *The Global Computer Industry Beyond Moore's Law: A Technical, Economic, and National Security Perspective*. Herndon, VA. January 14-15.

Thompson, Robert Luther. 1947. *Wiring a Continent: The History of the Telegraph Industry in the United States 1823-1836*. Princeton, N.J.: Princeton University Press.

Trauthwein, Christina. 2001. "You Say You Want a Revolution. . .." *Architectural Lighting*. May.

Tyson, Laura. 1992. *Who's Bashing Whom? Trade Conflict in High Tech Industries*. Washington, D.C.: Institute for International Economics.

U.S. Department of Commerce. 2002. *The Advanced Technology Program: Reform With a Purpose*. Washington, D.C.: U.S. Department of Commerce. February.

U.S. Department of Energy. 1995. *Alternative Futures for the Department of Energy National Laboratories*. The "Galvin Report." Washington, D.C.: U.S. Department of Energy.

U.S. Government Accounting Office. 1992. *SEMATECH's Technological Progress and Proposed R&D Program*. GAO/RCEED/92-223 BR. Washington, D.C.: U.S. Government Accounting Office. July.

U.S. Senate Committee on Appropriations. 1998. Report from the Committee on Appropriations to accompany Bill S. 2260. Washington, D.C.: United States Senate.

U.S. Senate Committee on Appropriations. 1998. *Senate Report 105-235*. Departments of Commerce, Justice, and State, the Judiciary, and Related Agencies Appropriation Bill. Washington, D.C.: United States Senate.

Varmus, Harold. 1999. "The Impact of Physics on Biology and Medicine." Plenary Talk, Centennial Meeting of the American Physical Society. Atlanta. March 22.

Vonortas, N.S. 1997. Cooperation in Research and Development. Norwell, MA: Klewer Academic Publishers.

Wolff , Alan Wm., Thomas R. Howell, Brent L. Bartlett, and R. Michael Gadbaw. eds. 1995. *Conflict Among Nations: Trade Policies in the 1990s*. San Francisco: Westview Press.

The World Bank. 1993. *The East Asian Economic Miracle: Economic Growth and Public Policy*. Policy Research Report. New York: Oxford University Press.

Zachary, G. Paschal. 1997. *Endless Frontier: Vannevar Bush, Engineer of the American Century*. New York: The Free Press.

Zchau, Ed. 1986. "Government Policies for Innovation and Growth" in National Research Council. *The Positive Sum Strategy: Harnessing Technology for Economic Growth*. Washington, D.C.: National Academy Press.